Patients

Say

The

Darndest

Things #3

Cool....a trilogy

William T. Sheahan MD

BookLocker.com, Inc.
2009

Dedication

I have a great mother.

"Family" has always been her #1 priority.

My mother is also a cancer survivor.

She has always modeled the importance of being resilient.

Therefore, whenever one of us has been "knocked down," we know we're expected to get back up.

It's what life is about and is one of the keys for having a fulfilling life on earth.

My wife and I have two children.

Both are just plain interesting.

Watching them grow up so far has been a joy, the extent of which I never could have predicted prior to becoming a father.

I'm pretty sure they know how much they are loved, despite my many moods and quirks, as well as how proud I am of them.

They are still too young to have read any of my books due to some of the content. When they get older and can better process the information, I'll give them copies. I'm sure they will then better understand why my wife (a pediatric nurse practitioner) and I have always let them know there's nothing they can say that will visibly shock us.

We both do a good job of keeping our poker faces on whenever needed.

FORWARD

Patients Say the Darndest Things #2 was dedicated to a close friend, Dennis Windmuller, who had been battling cancer for a number of years. He died on February 15, 2007. Prior to his death, his wife June asked his friends to write a letter about their experiences with Dennis over the years.

Dennis' best friend(s)

I used to think I was Dennis' best friend. He calls me frequently. He never identifies himself on the phone. He only has to say "Billy, Billy, Billy" or "What's up Doc" and I immediately know who it is. I always remember to call him on his birthday since we were both born on November 19th. He, on the other hand, always remembers to call on my wedding anniversary, the birthdays of my kids, and of course whenever Virginia Tech plays the University of Virginia (UVa). His phone calls have always been an amazing and greatly appreciated gift.

The truly amazing thing is that he does this for all his friends. We all feel as if we are his best friend.

I met Dennis in 1985 playing basketball at the Riverside Wellness Center. We were on the same team for a pick up game. He was loud and obnoxious and would pretty much take a long-range shot every time up the court, a very few of which went in. We lost the game.

He wasn't lacking for self confidence however.

I probably would have gone my separate way after the game but he wouldn't let me. I think his opening line was "so what's your story big man?"

We struck up a conversation and had some common ground. I was a resident physician and he was a pharmaceutical salesman. I also knew his Dad from the Health Department Pharmacy. We both liked sports.

I was amazed at how genuinely interested and engaging he was, especially after hearing so much trash talking during the game. He actually seemed like a decent guy, until we got outside and he found out I graduated from UVa. Immediately the trash talk started again as did the laughter when he saw my car. "You're a doctor for Pete's sake, why are you driving such a piece of shit for a car…oh that's right…you went to UVa, that explains it."

He always goes out of his way to be a perfect host. His hospital displays, sponsored educational talks and even parties at his home are always first class. He usually has enough food and drinks for a small army. He always makes sure everything is all set for his guests.

Years ago, we drove down together to a pharmaceutical company sponsored weekend in Pinehurst, NC. I was checking in at the desk when I overheard Dennis with another check-in clerk saying, "Windmuller, Dennis Windmuller, I'm with the pharmaceutical company that's hosting the event…you don't have a room reservation for me…you don't have any other rooms?"

We roomed together for the week-end. We had a great time. I even learned a little about a drug his company was promoting. I also got some insight into what living with Dennis must be like for June. I learned Dennis was even proud of a good fart. Most of us try to fart discretely. Not Dennis. He'll let you know when one is on the way, flip the covers up and then let it rip in your direction. We even played some golf.

There's nothing quite like a golf outing with Dennis. Anyone who has golfed with him will know what I'm talking about. A group of us used to go away for four days for an annual "Dali Lama" tournament. Some were excellent golfers-MacMasters, Clare, Russell and Napoleon-but most of us were hackers-Par-Triple Bogey-Quadruple Bogey-Par, etc. I would laugh so much during the weekend that my face would hurt. All topics were fair game for discussion. No holds barred: hair-color or lack thereof, weight, girlfriend, wife, and job. Occasionally an "outsider" would join us. They would either sink or swim. "Sink" and they wouldn't come back, or "swim" and they would instantly be brought into the group.

Over time we developed some classic golf rules. My favorite was for any shot that went into the woods. If you found a ball, you didn't have to count a penalty shot. Some of the best laughs came from hitting a white ball into the woods and a yellow ball back out of the woods. We also had a great time trying to "bag" each other. It's the art of unhooking the strap from around a person's golf bag so that it falls off when the cart moves forward. Dennis was a master of this skill, even before becoming a Master (the highest level of performance within his company) with his employer.

Dennis has always modeled the importance of finding fun in most things you do. He has shown me that it's great to laugh at others as well as yourself.

He's been amazingly successful in life and business, especially for someone who took seven years to graduate from Tech.

He's obviously been a great husband and father.

He's truly a wonderful guy. He has shown amazing courage, strength and dignity in his fight against cancer. He has remained a role model for life even while ill.

Dennis loves life and loves people.

Most of us go through life with a lot of acquaintances and a few true friends. Dennis has gone through life with a lot of "best friends."

If wealth could be measured by friends Dennis has to be the richest man I know.

I love you man. Thanks for allowing me to be one of your best friends.

Dennis was a great guy and an inspiration to all of us "knuckle-heads," as he used to affectionately call many of his friends. He will be greatly missed but never forgotten.

His motto for the last few years of his life was "faith-family-friends." Hopefully I'll be able to leave earth with such a wonderful legacy.

TABLE OF CONTENTS

INTRODUCTION

When I was younger I was a huge "Rocky" fan.

Although there were probably too many sequels to the original movie, I never got tired of the story line.

I guess that's my excuse for writing Patients Say the Darndest Things #3.

I'm sure the thousands of faithful readers of the first two books (okay, I admit to a huge exaggeration here) won't get tired of reading yet another installment!

Just as in book #2, I've included a lot of other stories as well.

Some medically related while others are more personal.

My writing style is definitely non-traditional (no paragraphs at times, etc). It's just the style I've adopted after years of charting in patients medical records.

It annoys my wife, especially since I need her to assist with grammar and punctuation, but she's still nice enough to help.

The pastor of our church frequently reminds us of the following:

We respect strength but we connect at weakness.

I hope we will be able to connect through some of these stories.

I also hope you'll get a few more laughs.

ONE: WHY ARE YOU SHOUTING AT ME?

The following dialogue occurred while interviewing a new patient. He was an 87 y/o male who lived in an assisted living facility. He wore hearing aids. A nursing aid from the facility presented with him.

Me: What's the name of the place where you live?

Patient: The Place.

Me (raising my voice a little): Yes, what's the name of the place?

Patient: The Place.

Me (at an even higher volume): DO YOU KNOW THE NAME OF THE PLACE WHERE YOU LIVE?

Patient: Yes, The Place. Why are you shouting at me?

Finally the nursing aid was nice enough to get me off the hook.

Nursing aid: Doctor, excuse me, the name of the assisted living facility is called "The Place."

Me: Oh…really? …thanks.

We all got to share a laugh after the exchange. It became apparent during the interview that he did have some memory impairment but he definitely knew where he lived!

I'm not sure what line of questioning to take when I ask this question in the future. Maybe I'll just start by asking "Do you live at The Place?"

TWO: PASTOR CARL

My wife and I were married 17 years ago by a friend of ours, Pastor Carl Cooper. We've kept in touch most recently through e-mail and he frequently sends some words of wisdom whenever possible. I want to pass along one of his recent e-mails, "Words to live by:"

1. Life isn't always fair, but it's still good.

2. When in doubt, just take the next small step.

3. Life is too short to waste time hating anyone.

4. Don't take yourself so seriously. No one else does.

5. Pay off your credit cards every month.

6. You don't have to win every argument. Agree to disagree.

7. Cry with someone. It's more healing than crying alone.

8. It's OK to get angry with God. He can take it.

9. Make peace with your past so it won't screw up the present.

10. Don't compare your life to others. You have no idea what their journey is all about.

11. If a relationship has to be a secret, you shouldn't be in it.

12. Everything can change in a blink of the eye. But don't worry; God never blinks.

13. Life is too short for long pity parties. Get busy living, or get busy dying.

14. A writer writes. If you want to be a writer, write.

15. Burn the candles, use the nice sheets. Don't save it for a special occasion. Today is special.

16. Be eccentric now. Don't wait for old age to wear purple.

17. The most important sex organ is the brain.

18. No one is in charge of your happiness except you.

19. Frame every so-called disaster with these words: "In five years, will it matter?"

20. Your children get only one childhood. Make it memorable.

21. Forgive everyone everything.

22. Envy is a waste of time. You already have all you need.

23. Don't audit life. Show up and make the most of it now.

24. No matter how you feel, get up, dress up and show up.

THREE: THE WAITING GAME

A few years ago our local newspaper (The Orlando Sentinel) ran a series of articles on the unacceptable waiting room times in most doctors' offices.

An editorial I wrote as a reply is attached below:

My wife and I spent a recent Saturday morning waiting for a piece of furniture to arrive. We were told it would arrive between 8 AM and 1 PM. We had to wait. It arrived at 12:55 PM.

My wife picked me up from work recently. I had left my car at the repair shop at 7 AM, but they were unable to get to it that day. "It should be ready tomorrow."

Although I needed 10 items from the grocery store, I put two back on the shelves so I could go through the "cash only, eight items or less" express lane. Unfortunately, the elderly woman ahead of me, with a full basket, who had to write a check, couldn't read the sign. I had to wait.

I got on the shortest line at McDonald's (I know, a doctor shouldn't be eating at such a place) because I was in a rush. Unfortunately, I didn't see the "trainee" tag under the employee's name. I had to wait.

On my way to the office I got behind a school bus. I had to wait.

My second patient today called in urgently and had to be seen because of an "ear infection." We spent 30 minutes together. She is having financial difficulties, her mother is dying of cancer, a daughter is abusing street drugs, and she and her husband are having problems communicating and with intimacy. Her ears were normal.

My third patient arrived on time. Unfortunately he had to wait. My staff and I apologized. I hope we will catch up later.

FOUR: TESTS AND MORE TESTS

Here are a few common scenarios:

* An elderly male is evaluated in an emergency room with a transient neurologic deficit of some kind. He undergoes a head CT through the ER. Soon after, he undergoes an MRI, MRA, carotid Doppler, an echocardiogram and sometimes a trans-esophageal echocardiogram. He is sometimes discharged on just aspirin therapy.

He underwent thousands of dollars of tests and is sent home on a medication that costs pennies a day.

* A person presents to a hospital with chest pain. An EKG, chest x-ray and labs are done. Often a chest CT is done to rule out a pulmonary embolus. A treadmill stress test may be done. A nuclear cardiac scan may follow. Finally, due to some minor abnormalities, a cardiac catheterization may be done. Sometimes the cardiac catheterization is normal or doesn't show any significant change from one done previously (sometimes only months prior).

He/she is often sent home on aspirin and/or the same medications they took prior to the hospitalization.

* A chest x-ray is performed. The radiologist feels there might be an abnormality present and recommends additional views. The additional views are inconclusive. A chest CT scan is recommended. The chest CT scan is also inconclusive. A PET scan is recommended. The PET scan is also inconclusive.

9

Therefore, chest CT scans are recommended every 6 months for the next couple of years.

In addition, a note is made on the initial chest x-ray of an abnormality possibly seen in the shoulder as well as an abnormal calcification in the upper abdomen.

And…additional diagnostic studies are recommended to evaluate these abnormalities.

Sometimes, after many thousands of dollars, and significant radiation exposure, you find all is fine…nothing to worry about.

Many tests and many high tech procedures exist.

I'm not against doing tests at all. It's just that in many cases, nothing is done with the information or therapy doesn't change.

Try to avoid cook-book work-ups whenever possible.

Try to consider if a test will really change therapy or outcome.

Consider when close clinical follow-up (the old fashioned approach) may be more appropriate than an additional barrage of tests.

FIVE: ALL SORTS OF TESTS

Despite the high tech world in which we live, effective communication is often lacking in the medical care that is being rendered these days.

I live in a suburb of a relatively big city with competing hospitals every few miles outlining the city.

For over the last ten years I have practiced outpatient medicine.

Folks come to our clinic from all over the area.

When a patient (who is at my office) needs to be hospitalized I complete a transfer note that lists the presenting symptoms and any applicable outpatient evaluation, as well as any other pertinent information (past medical history, chronic medications, etc.).

I call the hospital emergency room (just up the street) and discuss the case with a triage nurse as well as the ER physician and/or the hospitalist.

Usually I am able to get updates on how things are going as well as being informed when they are being discharged home.

Records are sent or faxed to my attention.

Many times, however, patients are admitted to other hospitals (due to an emergency or being out of town) and I was never informed that they were hospitalized.

Here's a typical office dialogue with a patient who returns to my office after such a hospitalization:

Me: I'm sorry you were sick but hope you're feeling better. What happened while you were in the hospital?

Patient: Didn't you get any records? I told them you were my primary care doctor.

Me: No, not yet. In the future it's always a good idea to hand carry the records to me.

Patient: Hey wait...they gave me these papers. Maybe these will help.

He/she then pulls out some crumbled up pieces of paper. Usually the "papers" consist of a hand written, poorly legible copy of a medication reconciliation sheet (the medications they were discharged on) and some computer generated medication information sheets.

Me: No, these aren't really helpful. What doctor took care of you while you were there?

Patient: I can't remember. There were so many of them. Some had accents and others spoke perfect English. A lot of times they said they were assistants working for a doctor. I kept going for a bunch of tests.

Me: What kind of tests?

Patient: All sorts of tests. They did x-rays and stuff in the ER and then I had a bunch of other tests. They put some jelly on my skin and rubbed a sound stick over it, put me through the donut shaped machine and then did one of those magnetic rotating isolating tests. They even used a balloon to open a blood vessel before they put in one of those splints to keep it open.

Me: OK, you had an ultrasound, a CT scan, a MRI (magnetic resonance imaging) and had a stent placed.

How did everything turn out?

Patient: I guess alright. I didn't get to talk to the doctors before I went home. A nurse came to my room about 10 o'clock (PM) and said the doctor called and that I could go home. I needed to leave before midnight so I wouldn't get charged for another day. I asked to talk to the doctor, or one of the assistants, but was told they were all too busy right now. The nurse said my primary doctor would be able to get all the information.

Above sound familiar (for others practicing outpatient medicine)?

If not, aren't you lucky?

I haven't been as fortunate as you.

This type of scenario plays out many times during a typical month with the patients I see.

Sometimes it gets even more comical. Especially when they've received bills from the hospital and the providers who rendered care (often within days), for thousands of dollars, but they still don't know exactly what went on.

Here's what I try to always explain to patients I see:

-I'm sorry I only practice outpatient medicine at this time (that might change again in the future).

-Please contact me whenever you are admitted to another hospital and give the physician caring for you (or someone on his staff) permission to call me and discuss your case both during the hospitalization and prior to being discharged.

-You need to take the initiative to get health care personnel to explain things. Even if a fully dictated note can't be obtained right away you should never leave ANY medical facility without a basic understanding of what was done and what was found.

-If you feel things haven't been answered to your satisfaction you need to ask for assistance. All medical centers have patient advocates so use them when needed.

-It's your responsibility to obtain your own records.

-All the doctors, at all the hospitals in the area we live, do not dialogue with each other every day. In fact, we don't usually even know each other personally.

-When you obtain your records, I will review them completely and then try to explain everything in as simple terms as needed.

-You should always keep a file of your records as well. It makes no sense to keep accurate records of your car repairs while not doing the same for your health records.

SIX: THE TINY CELL

A local radio personality does an advertisement for an imaging center.

"Set up an appointment as soon possible for your whole-body CT scan. I did and it saved my life."

He never goes into the details of what was found or how it saved his life, however.

Another imaging center, in our town, runs a different type of radio commercial. It goes something like this, "It starts as a tiny cell, obtains a complex blood supply, and then spreads uncontrollably throughout your body…cancer; we're talking about cancer. Call today for your whole-body CT scan; it will give you peace of mind."

Patients ask me all the time if they should have one done.

I went ahead and called one of the imaging centers. The multi-slice whole-body CT scan exam costs $900.

$900 isn't too bad for some peace of mind (especially for a rich doctor such as me).

I still haven't had one yet.

I do think early detection of many cancers is worthwhile.

However, I recently read an article written by a health editor for a magazine. He went to an exclusive wellness center/health spa and part of his stay included the whole-body CT.

Prior to leaving he had a review of all the studies done. The CT scan showed abnormalities in the lung, liver and prostate. He was told that these would need further evaluation.

He spent the next few months wondering if he had cancer, seeing specialists and having additional tests and biopsies performed. Ultimately, all was fine. The lung lesion was scar tissue, the liver lesion was a cyst and the prostate abnormality was a benign growth.

He was relieved to get the news.

He had spent a lot of time worrying.

He couldn't help but wonder why he had gone through the whole-body CT scan in the first place.

I could see his point.

However, I'm still not sure what I'll do.

I want to be around for as long as possible for my family.

But, I also hate to be poked and probed unless necessary.

I hate being "a patient."

But, I also hate to think about "that tiny cell that obtains a blood supple and grows uncontrollably throughout my body."

Gee, I wonder if that's what the advertising guru's were hoping for…

For now, I try to refer folks to the Food and Drug Administration (FDA) website. It states the following:

"The FDA has never approved CT for screening any part of the body for any specific disease, let alone for screening the whole body when there are no specific symptoms of a disease at all. No manufacturer has submitted data to the FDA to support the safety and efficacy of screening claims for whole-body CT screening."

It also states "…the FDA knows of no data demonstrating that whole-body CT screening is effective in detecting any particular disease early enough for the disease to be managed, treated, or cured and advantageously spare a person at least some of the detriment associated with serious illness or premature death."

SEVEN: A GORILLA AS A PET

I fill out MANY forms for my patients.

Family medical leave forms, disability parking forms, etc, etc.

I recently had a first.

I was asked to fill out a special form for a female patient.

She wanted to be allowed to have a cat as a pet.

She lived in a no-pet senior citizen apartment complex.

She had some medical and psychiatric problems and the mental health professionals thought the cat would be a good companion and could help her emotionally.

The form was entitled the "Fair Housing Act."

Its purpose was to allow for accommodations for individuals with disabilities.

The questions seemed relatively straight forward.

I think I made a note on the form along the lines of "It seems reasonable to allow this person to have a cat if possible. I feel that a pet would serve as a good companion and would help her emotionally."

Later that day I ran into a colleague.

He had never filled out such a form.

He asked what I did. I told him.

He agreed that it seemed like a reasonable approach.

He went on the say, "it's not like she was asking to have a gorilla, or something, as a pet."

"Well said," I thought.

We both laughed.

However, I decided not to amend the form to include his statement. I figured the housing authority folks might not have the same sense of humor.

EIGHT: MEDICAL COUNTRY-WESTERN SONGS

Sometimes I like country western songs.

I enjoy the fact that I can often understand what is being sung, unlike many other types of music.

Sometimes the lyrics are pretty sad.

"My dog died, my car broke down, my tires are flat, and my girlfriend left me for my brother."

I know this might not sound appropriate but I can often hear the makings of an excellent country song while taking some social histories.

A recent encounter with a 22 y/o male is an example:

Patient: I'm under a lot of stress.

Me: What's up?

Patient: I met some guys and was able to make some quick money selling crack but we all got busted. I've already spent some time in but may have more jail time coming up.

Me: Sorry to hear.

Patient: I sort of got in over my head. Now my town house is in foreclosure and my car got repossessed. I've got to go to court next week.

Me: For the drug charges?

Patient: No, for something else. I got involved with someone I shouldn't have been with and she's taking me to court to enforce a paternity test. She says I'm the father of one of her kids.

Me: You do have a lot going on.

I have empathy for most of my patients. However, I didn't have the heart to tell him that I couldn't get the lyrics of a possible new medical country-western song out of my head.

"Got busted for crack, had my home foreclosed, my car got repossessed, and someone I shouldn't have been with says I fathered her child."

NINE: THE SMOKING VAN

One day I was walking to my car after a long day in the office.

I sensed that I was being followed.

I turned around twice and it was a van with darkly tinted windows.

I decided I would start to run only if I heard the engine starting to race.

It pulled up close to me.

I stood still and tried not to look too nervous.

Finally, the driver rolled down a window.

He had a cigarette in his mouth and smoke came billowing out the window.

"Dr. Sheahan, Dr. Sheahan, I thought it was you. I need your help."

"Oh hi, I didn't recognize you at first. What can I do to help?"

"I need a stress test. My younger sister just found out she has heart disease. She had a stress test done and it was abnormal. Now she's getting ready to have a catheterization. We've pretty much had the same problems over the years. Whatever one of us has, the other also has."

"I'll be happy to help you. All my staff has left for the day but I'll set up an appointment as soon as possible. Are you having any chest pain?"

"No, none whatsoever," he said after taking another drag of the cigarette in his hand.

I started to laugh.

"I'm not laughing at you, just the circumstances. I'm glad you're concerned about your health. You mentioned that you and your sister are alike in all ways. Does she also drive around smoking in her car, with the windows closed, while worrying about her heart as well?"

"I know; it looks sort of bad, doesn't it? I'm trying to stop…and yes, she does smoke."

"No problem, I'll try to help you quit again as well. I'm glad it was you. I wasn't sure if you were a friend or foe when I looked around and saw a van with dark windows following me."

He laughed.

TEN: JUST HELPING TO PAY A FEW OF THE BILLS

A 48 y/o male came in requesting an HIV test.

Me: What are your concerns?

Patient: I've been seeing a couple of girls for some time now but I just met another nice girl at church. She won't have sex with me until I get an HIV test and show her the results.

Me: Were the girls you were seeing with other men as well?

Patient: How am I supposed to know? I've never asked them.

Me: Did you have to pay to have sexual relations with them?

Patient: No! They aren't prostitutes! They're even roommates. I never had to pay them to have sex with me...sometimes they might ask for me to help with some of the bills but it's no big deal.

Me: What kind of bills?

Patient: You know...the utilities, sometimes the phone bill, sometimes the electric bill, you know how it is, right?

Me: Yes, I do. Getting tested is a good idea for now but even if you test negative you will still need to be retested in a few months to make sure you haven't been exposed.

We then spent some time reviewing sexually transmitted diseases in as much detail as possible, but also in very simplistic terms.

I decided not to discuss what I was really thinking about the girls.

I suspect that he was probably just one of many men they see to help pay some of the bills!

ELEVEN: WOULD HAVE NEVER THUNK IT

I saw an 84 y/o male for follow-up of his blood pressure.

Prior to finishing, his "oh, by the way complaint" was a rash around his privates.

I looked briefly and he had redness and irritation around the inguinal area. I told him to use an over-the-counter antifungal cream.

He returned about a week later with increased itching in the same region.

Closer inspection revealed pubic lice.

Me: Have you had any new sexual relationships lately?

Patient: No, I've been married for 61 years. Why?

Me: You have pubic lice. I'm not sure how you could have gotten it.

Patient: (immediately gets teary eyed and keeps his eyes down) I hate to say it, my wife would leave me...I've been spending time on the computer lately and got involved in something...I got into a chat room and got invited to a party for swingers...and I went.

Me: What happened?

Patient: I had sex with a number of different people at the party.

Me: (trying to not appear too shocked) Oh, that's probably where you caught it. How many people were you with?

Patient: About three or four.

We then had quite a long discussion.

I really just wanted to say "Wow, I would have never thunk it for a million years."

I not sure if I was more shocked at the fact that he, at 84 years old, went to the party for swingers or that he had relations with three or four people on the same night, especially after reviewing his medications and noting that I had never prescribed Viagra, Levitra or Cialis!

TWELVE: ALL IN THE DAY

- 51 y/o male presented with a strained lower back:

Me: How did you hurt yourself?

Patient: I was vacuuming out my daughter's car at a do-it-yourself car wash. It's a small car and I was trying to do it quickly because it costs 50 cents a minute and didn't want to spend any more money than I needed to.

- Letter received from a thoughtful patient:

"Hi, I'm back in jail again for trespassing, two counts. I will be here anywhere from 60-120 days so I'll miss my next appointment. I'll re-contact you to make a follow-up appointment once I get out. Best wishes to you as always."

- 72 y/o male:

Patient: My mother is 95 years old and has macular degeneration. I've been praying that she improves her diet and I've really been tough on her lately. I let her know that she probably wouldn't have so many medical problems if she started to take better care of herself.

- 77 y/o male:

"I've always thought I should've been a doctor but I didn't have the schooling. I've been a mechanic my whole life. I think being a doctor would be easier. Car engines change every year but the human body stays the same."

I wasn't exactly sure what to say as a comeback but I know what I was thinking: at least cars can't talk!

- 53 y/o male:

Patient: Can having sex raise your blood pressure? (I was still thinking of my answer when he continued) If so, you need to know that I got some right before coming in for this appointment today.

- 78 y/o male:

Me: It's great to see you.

Patient: It's great to be seen. In twelve years I'll be 90.

It was also good to know he could still do some simple math!

- 66 y/o male with an enlarged prostate:

Patient: I went ahead and saw the dicksmith you asked me to see.

Me: The dicksmith?

Patient (laughing): The urologist...you know the dicksmith, sort of like a locksmith.

- 58 y/o male with Peyronie's disease of the penis (a fibrous plaque of the corpora cavernosa of the penis that causes the penis to curve with an erection):

Me: Was the urologist able to go over everything with you?

Patient: Yeah, he said I have a fiberous plague on the porous cave of my penis.

Me: That's close. Let me write down the name of the condition so that you can look it up for yourself as well.

THIRTEEN: THE RHYMING MAN

My Nurse: Dr. Sheahan, there's a man in the waiting room who's talking out loud and rhyming nonstop. Can I bring him back to an empty room? The other patients are complaining about him!

Me: Sure.

After getting up some "courage" I went into the room with him.

Me: Hi, how is everything going?

Patient (a 22 y/o male): If you want to know, you better have a fro.

Me: Are you alright?

Patient: I'm alright but you're not too bright.

Me (after laughing): Are you aware that you rhyme?

Patient: I'm aware so you better beware, to make it you must take it, I'm alive, that's no jive.

After a minute or more of nonstop rhyming I needed to excuse myself.

Me: I'll be right back.

Patient: I'll be right here on this rack, Jack.

One of my mental health colleagues agreed to see him for an evaluation. My nurse escorted him to the psychiatrist's office.

For the rest of the day I had a recurring thought:

"He needed to see a shrink, I think!"

FOURTEEN: JUST NOT LIKE IT USED TO BE

A 60 y/o male appeared slightly depressed.

Me: Is everything alright?

Patient: The world is so different.

Me: What do you mean?

Patient: People are different. It's just not like it used to be. People don't seem to have any values anymore. I was raised by my grandmother and she taught me values. I have so little hope in people that I choose to not associate with them. I prefer to just stay at home instead of going out to do anything.

Me: What sort of things did you used to enjoy doing?

Patient: I used to enjoy going out to a nice nightclub…drinking a few beers…going to spend a couple thousand dollars gambling at a casino…having a girl for a few hours…not to spend the whole night…just a couple of hours for some fun before heading back home to my wife and family.

I can't remember exactly what I said in response to his statement.

Most likely it was something along the lines of "Hmm, I see," a statement that any psychiatrist would have been proud to see me make.

I was having a harder time processing what he had said as well as reviewing the changes in our society's values that had him so concerned.

It appears he was upset about the lack of:

1. Partying

2. Alcohol consumption

3. Gambling

And last, but not least,

4. Adultery & prostitution

FIFTEEN: HAVING A HARD TIME TRYING TO VISUALIZE

A male with chronic back pain also has erectile dysfunction.

He has tried multiple treatments but most recently has been using a product called MUSE. It's a drug eluding pellet that is inserted into the urethra to help obtain an erection.

Me: How has everything been going?

Patient: OK. The MUSE has been working out fine. I still can't get off but at least it gets hard enough for my wife to back into me.

Me: Back into you? What do you mean?

Patient: I can't mount her because of my back but I'm able to set my walker right up against the side of the bed. She's then able to scoot back up against the walker doggie style and back into me. I'm just happy to be able to do the man thing and bring pleasure to my wife.

Sometimes I wonder why I had to ask an additional question.

It certainly crossed my mind in this circumstance.

I did sort of chuckle to myself thinking what a difficult drawing this would be for an illustrator if this fellow ever agreed to be included in a "sex book" for folks with disabilities.

They would probably just have to include a photograph.

SIXTEEN: OKAY THEN

A 51 y/o male presented for the first time. He was a thin male who appeared "wired" and he had a moist, clammy handshake.

Me: Welcome, I'm glad you're here. What brings you to the clinic today?

Patient: I need help. If you only knew the depths of my mind right now you would be afraid to be in the same room as me. I can't stop thinking about wanting to hurt myself and killing those around me. I carry a rope in my car just so that if a day arrives and I feel ready I can pull up along the side of the road, find a good tree and hang myself. I'm surprised I drove myself here and even left the house to come to this appointment because I usually get a feeling of rage whenever I drive by someone on the road that looks happy. Sometimes I fantasize about running people down with my truck. I dream almost every night about strangling people. I don't watch TV because I want to kill all the punks.

Me: Okay then...any other concerns?

Patient: Yeah, I've been having ringing in my ears; I also need to get my eyes examined for new glasses and I've lost interest in sex.

Me: Give me a minute or two, I'll be right back. I'm sure I'll be able to help with your eyes and ears but I need to call a colleague to assist me in trying to help you with your initial concerns.

I was able to get in touch with a mental health colleague and fortunately, Charles Manson's protégé, I mean the patient, agreed to an acute psychiatric hospitalization for evaluation and stabilization.

I'm not the smartest guy in the world but I was able to figure out a few things about his other stated concerns:

1. Maybe he'll have a little more interest in sexual relations once he (hopefully) stops feeling as if he wants to kill everybody.

2. I didn't immediately ask for consults with the optometrist and audiologist. I was pretty sure that they would appreciate not evaluating this patient until he was feeling "better."

On further reflection, only one thought came to mind: "Wow."

SEVENTEEN: OKAY THEN #2

I was asked by a mental health colleague to do a medical clearance on a 50 y/o male who was acutely intoxicated.

I had never seen him before.

He was on five different mental health medications.

He had multiple psychiatric diagnoses, bipolar disorder and schizoaffective disorder to name a few.

He was with his wife. She did almost all the talking.

He looked much older than his stated age.

She reported him drinking at least a half gallon of vodka a day for a number of days.

He was sitting in a wheelchair, disheveled and naked except for wearing a small blue pair of shorts.

His wife had come home from work and found him slumped over a couch and with slurred speech.

She noted that he had been having auditory and visual hallucinations.

She noted that he had been talking out loud to his father who had died over twenty years ago.

She let me know that he wasn't suicidal.

She then let me know that he was only homicidal.

I asked what she meant.

She went on to say that he has ongoing thoughts about needing to kill someone, anyone, preferably a stranger.

She said he felt he needed to do this to release his inner demons.

He was seeing the psychiatrist for this concern.

I then turned to the patient and asked if he remembered my name.

He replied "Why?"

"Because I want to try to make sure you don't think of me as a stranger," I replied.

To my surprise, he grinned and then even laughed a little bit.

EIGHTEEN: JUST NEED A LITTLE BREAK

Years ago a survey appeared in the Journal Cortlandt Forum (July 2006).

It was a survey to physicians that asked:

"How often are you asked to give informal medical advice while attending social events?"

The results were as follows:

22% all the time

48% regularly

25% not often

5% enough so that I avoid social events

Even more amusing to me was a statement made by one of the participants in the survey, Dr. Krishman from Mayfield Heights, Ohio:

"Being asked for medical advice at a social event is part of being a doctor. The public is under the delusion that we are actually interested in everybody's personal medical issues, even when they are not our patients."

Perhaps initially this statement seems a little harsh, especially for some non-medical folks. To me it's funny.

I do believe that most medical professionals care about their fellow man, even when they aren't their patients.

However, I also know that there are times when I just need a little break from medicine.

Sometimes I'm just tired of talking or tired of having people talk to me.

NINETEEN: MY HAIRCUT WITH PEARL

My wife called me at work.

"The person who was going to cut your hair (for my son and I) called in sick but you have an appointment with someone named Pearl. I think it might be an older woman."

"That's fine with me," I replied, "I don't care who cuts our hair. Why do you think it's an older woman?"

"Her name is Pearl. Have you come across a young person with the name Pearl lately?"

When we arrived she was an older woman. I'm not sure how old she was but I suspect she was at least in her mid 60's.

"You must be Bill and Tom," she said while looking at the appointment book, "Who wants to go first?"

Tom went back with her.

I could hear her saying "it's good to meet you, Brent. Have I cut your hair before, Brent?"

My son's hair cut took about 40 minutes. He gave me some "what's up" and "why me" glances whenever she would excuse herself.

She had to leave while cutting his hair to go to the bathroom, to say hello to a friend who walked through the hair establishment, and to get a band aid for the finger she accidently cut with her scissors.

Now it was my turn.

"You look like an accountant, are you an accountant?"

"Oh no, I'm not."

"What do you do for a living?"

"I'm a doctor."

I know it was a pretty stupid response for someone who prefers to be incognito at times such as this.

"Do you like cats?" she then asked.

"Sure" I said. (It was a huge lie.)

"I could tell you were someone special and you look caring. Let me tell you about my cat. My father in law came to live with us a few years ago. He was 100 years old and his doctors said he didn't have very long to live. He loved my cat. My father in law spent most of his day in a wheelchair. The cat stayed on his lap most of the day. We would even put a hot dog in his shirt pocket most days and the cat would climb up his chest and eat the hot dog from the shirt pocket. My father in law came to live with us in January 2004. He wasn't supposed to live long but he lived until this past February. He died when he was 103 years old. I think it was the cat the kept him living for so long. And guess what...Are you still listening to me?"

"Oh, ah, yes," I replied.

"Exactly one week after my father in law died my cat died. Can you believe it? Exactly one week after my father in law died, God rest his soul, my cat died. I couldn't help to think my father in law came back and asked the cat to join him. I asked my son, who used to be a Rabbi but is now a dairy farmer. He said yes, he thinks the cat decided to join my father in law. He said that animals were God's original creatures and that the cat has a cat soul and is a very highly honored member of God's family. Humans have a human soul but cats have an animal soul. Both souls can communicate and both are God's creation. This topic makes me so emotional that it's hard to concentrate on your haircut. My son studied for many years and was a good Rabbi but he has seven kids and couldn't support his family so he decided to become a dairy farmer. He raises organic cows only and sells only to places like Whole Foods. The cows only eat pure food. I told him he should advertise that his cows are grass fed only. Don't you think that would be a good slogan for his company? Grass fed cows. I think it's sort of a catchy phrase. He was doing really well until gas prices started to rise. It's tough on everyone but especially for small business owners although he isn't really a small business. He supplies milk to almost 30 stores throughout Florida. Thirty stores. That's a lot isn't it? You should really think about buying your food from his stores. It's much healthier. You could even tell your patients. Too many pesticides are being used in other food. All his children are so smart. I think it's because they have been drinking his milk for so long…"

After about 40 minutes my haircut was finished.

"I really enjoyed talking with you," Pearl said. "I hope you will let me cut your hair in the future. I knew you would appreciate my stories since you're a doctor."

"You bet," I said as my son and I hurried from our haircut adventure out the door and to our car. I lied. I think I'll have to go to a completely different hair establishment; at least until Pearl joins her cat (just kidding).

When I told the story to my wife she laughed and said "why did you tell her you were a doctor? You should've known better than that."

TWENTY: FAMILY WALKS

Sometimes, however, talking is good and therapeutic.

We've lived in the same house since 1993.

Both of our children have been born since we moved there.

We have a two-mile loop around our neighborhood.

We've walked the loop hundreds of times.

When the kids were infants my wife and I would use it for exercise and for a time to just talk since the kids would usually sleep in the stroller.

As the kids have gotten older we continue to use it for some quality family time.

I highly recommend it to all families.

All families need to have some time away from the TV, computer, phone, mail, bills, cleaning, dirty dishes and laundry.

We often start out quiet.

Many times there was inertia to go and one or another initially resented being asked to take a walk.

Sometimes we have some minor arguments or disagreements along the way.

For the most part, however, we usually work things out by the time we get back to our home.

Everyone feels better.

Most importantly, we have reconnected about some of the crazy things that have occurred in our day, both good and bad, that would not have been a topic of conversation without a walk.

TWENTY-ONE: SAY WHAT?

- An 86 y/o male had complaints of erectile dysfunction:

Patient: My wife always said if she died first she hoped that I wouldn't be able to get an erection with any other women. Well, she got her wish.

- I asked a 73 y/o male if he had any hearing problems:

Patient: I've never had a problem with ear wax (I didn't ask him if he did but I let him continue). My poodle loves to stick her tongue in my ears everyday and I think this helps to keep them real clean.

I was about to comment when he went on to further add "and she (the poodle) also seems to like the taste of my deodorant a lot."

I was tempted to call the animal abuse hot line but decided to just "let it go."

- 67 y/o male requested a prescription for Viagra:

Me: Has it been helpful?

Patient: Yeah, I've been using it for years with my girlfriend.

A little while later he mentioned that he thinks he has a rash from a new laundry detergent that his wife has been using.

Me: Wife?

Patient: Yeah, I'm married and so is my girlfriend. We've been having sex about 2-3 times a month for the last 20 years or so.

Me: How have you kept it a secret for so long?

Patient: Her husband thinks she goes shopping a lot and my wife thinks I play a lot of golf.

TWENTY-TWO: WORKING IN
AN ICE CREAM FACTORY

I'm not a sex therapist but I often spend a lot of my day trying to play one.

I'm not embarrassed about discussing sexual related issues with patients nor am I shy about asking for details, and if possible, offering advice.

I recently saw a 44 year-old man who presented with his wife. After the usual pleasantries we got down to the reason for the visit.

He and his wife were concerned about his lack of libido and desire for sexual relations.

His wife was very pretty.

Unlike many couples that I see, they seemed to have a respectful communication style and I sensed they truly cared for each other.

His "plumbing" was intact and still functioned well when called into action. He just didn't want to use it very frequently.

They had been married for three years. His first wife had died of renal failure. It was the second marriage for both of them. They were financially secure. Their extended families had merged well and all children were grown and out on their own. Both worked and seemed to enjoy their jobs. Both reported "healthy" sexual habits in the past.

I was about to launch into a discussion about decreased sexual desire when I decided to ask one additional question: Is anything else new or different?

That's when they offered they had become nudists a few years ago (right after they were married) and had lived in a nudist colony for the last two years.

Being curious and naïve about a nudist colony I got some more information. They did EVERYTHING in the nude. Walked in the nude, golfed and played tennis in the nude, swam in the nude, went to the on-site shopping center in the nude, etc, etc.

I can honestly say this was a new one for me.

I didn't have a whole lot of things to offer at the time in terms recommendations.

His physical exam was normal.

I sent him to the lab to check some routine laboratory studies as well as a testosterone level.

That night it hit me...I think.

It's sort of like a person that works in an ice cream shop who doesn't have any interest in eating ice cream.

I love seeing my wife nude because most of the time she has her clothes on. It's one of my simple joys of life. Even after 17 years of marriage, it remains pretty darn exciting.

However, I'm pretty sure some of the novelty would wear off if we spent our entire time nude. Eventually, I suspect that I would lose a bit of interest in being intimate as well.

All of his labs returned with normal results, including his testosterone level. When I saw them back I recommend that they seek some counseling together to more thoroughly investigate possible emotional issues. I didn't think it was appropriate to tell them to occasionally put their clothes back on.

I give them a lot of credit. It's pretty cool they feel so comfortable being nude all the time, especially around others.

It's just not for me.

Perhaps it would be more appealing if I could be assured that the swimming pool water wasn't too cold. Otherwise I might be too self conscious about the "shrinkage factor."

I still look OK nude, by candlelight, especially with my gut sucked in.

I also still love ice cream.

TWENTY-THREE: SPEAKING OF INTIMACY ISSUES

I've had many conversations with patients over the last twenty years on the topic of intimacy and sexual relations in general.

I do have some personal views, for any interested married males, that I may as well share. Any others will need to come in for a private consultation so I can get some specifics about your particular situation.

1. Improve your foreplay (for many women, this may consist of everything that has happened in the previous 24 hours):

    a. Always try to communicate respectfully. Apologize when it's appropriate and show that you mean it.

    b. Be helpful around the house with chores, errands, and driving the kids to activities. Many surveys report that some women think it's a "turn on" to see their husband doing housework. I've tried to become a housework expert after reading these surveys.

    c. Exercise together-take walks, go to the gym and even get in touch with your feminine side by taking dance classes, yoga and Pilates.

    d. Show her that you can be affectionate without expecting anything in return. Compliment her looks, clothing, hair style and most of all; thank her every day for being a great wife and mother.

2. As for intimacy itself:

   a. Be observant. Lay off when you see any monthly "feminine products" on display.

   b. Be OK with the fact the she holds most of the cards unless you're someone that just wants to hop on and do "your thing."

   c. Don't be stupid. If your wife is closed for business, don't venture elsewhere.

   d. Be alert to clues, both good and bad:

      1. Good signs: When she comes to bed naked and gives you a really long kiss as she says goodnight...duh!

      2. Bad signs: When she gives you a quick "peck" as she says goodnight and turns on her side, facing away from you, when touched anywhere. Take either of these "hints" as a sign that the day is officially over.

And finally, if you want to perform like Tarzan you need to make your wife feel like Jane, the Queen of the Jungle. She needs to trust you completely. Don't give her any reason to think otherwise. Hopefully you will then remain the King of the Jungle for many, many years to come.

TWENTY-FOUR: YOU DON'T SAY

1. A 74 y/o female: My father would still be alive today if all his doctors hadn't screwed up.

Me: When did he die?

Patient: Almost ten years ago.

Me: How old was he when he died?

Patient: 98.

2. A 48 y/o male: The oxy (oxycontin) took my manhood away but now that I'm off and my hard-on's are back I'm chasing my wife around the house to get some.

3. Patient: I'm having trouble performing ever since my wife said my penis was cute.

Me: Why do you think you're having such a problem with what she said?

Patient: Because she was married before and I think it's her own way of telling me it's much smaller than her ex-husbands.

4. Patient: I'm having trouble satisfying my wife and need help.

Me: What sort of problem are you having?

Patient: Basically I can't last long enough. My wife keeps telling me to not bother to start something I can't finish.

5. Patient (A 82 y/o male): My marriage was recently annulled.

Me: How long were you married?

Patient: 6 weeks.

Me: What happened?

Patient: She couldn't stand my passing gas so often.

Me: Is that a new problem?

Patient: No, but it wasn't until we were married and had some time alone that she knew I had a problem. Most of our dates before we were married were at social events and the noise level kept her from knowing I was farting.

6. Patient (A 64 y/o male): I keep hearing about ED on the TV. I have IDW.

Me: IDW?

Patient (after laughing): It Don't Work!

7. The Patient is a 65 y/o male that has been having marital problems.

Me: How long have you been married?

Patient: She's my 4th wife...I brought her on to the mother ship for the first time about 25 years ago.

Me (wondering if he was talking about his sexual organ or something else...I decided to go for the "something else"): Are you a Star Wars fan?

8. A 53 y/o male returned to me after having recently seen an orthopedic surgeon due to shoulder pain.

Me: How did everything go?

Patient: Fine, he gave me an injection but boy did it hurt. You want to hear something funny?

Me: Sure.

Patient: When I told the doctor that the injection hurt he said "that's funny; it didn't hurt me a bit."

We both laughed. I let him know that I would need to use the same phrase in the future. It was a perfect response if you ask me.

9. A patient has high cholesterol. She was started on treatment a number of months ago. Lab tests show that her cholesterol remains elevated.

Me: Have you been pretty good about taking your cholesterol medication?

Patient: Yes, I've got the medication at my house.

Me: Are you actually taking it?

Patient: Honestly, not very often.

Me: I'll take the blame for that. I guess I forgot to tell you that you needed to swallow it, in addition to having it at our house.

Patient (smiling): Yeah, it's your fault. I guess I'll take it now that that you finally educated me.

10. An 83 y/o male came in for a follow-up appointment.

Patient: I was initially upset that it took so long to get in to see the optometrist but it ended up being a blessing.

Me: How come?

Patient: I went to the Hard Rock Casino recently in Tampa to visit with my daughter. I played video poker and discarded the wrong cards because my vision was blurry but ended up getting four 4's and won $250. I wouldn't have won if I was seeing clearly because I would have kept the Aces that I accidently discarded.

11. A 70 y/o Hispanic male came in for a new patient visit.

Patient: Do you speak Spanish?

Me: Just a little bit. Do you need me to get a translator?

Patient: No, we should be alright if I just have a little shit.

Me: I'm sorry, what do you need?

Patient: A little shit so I can write things down that I may not pronounce correctly.

Me: You bet. I'll get you a sheet of paper.

12. Patient: I don't drink alcohol at all but occasionally have a little wine.

13. 58 y/o male.

Patient (smiling): Doc, I was a little upset when I saw your note asking for me to be set up for a fuck-you appointment. Luckily, the clerk at the front was able to let me know that an F-U appointment was a follow-up appointment. I'm originally from New Jersey and up there "F-U" only means one thing!

14. 52 y/o male appeared to have the wrong height listed on his chart.

Me: How tall are you?

Patient: About 5 foot, 10 inches (70 inches).

Me: I thought so, my nurse listed you at 60 inches; I need to give you an additional 10 inches.

Patient: Boy, my ex-wife sure would have liked me to have another 10 inches!

He laughed first and then I did also.

TWENTY-FIVE: DO YOU THINK HE HAS A FAVORITE WORD?

A 66 y/o male wanted to voice a concern.

He had undergone a laser procedure a number of years ago for an enlarged prostate.

He had a thick New York accent but talked in a calm voice:

"The fuckin doctor up north fuckin screwed me up...when I have a big-o (orgasm) it fuckin goes in instead of out...then I have to get it out of me by fuckin peeing...it still fuckin feels the same but if God wanted it to go back fuckin inside he would have fuckin made us that way in the fuckin first place."

We then had a good discussion on retrograde ejaculation and I made some recommendations.

At the conclusion of his visit he wanted to let me know one last thing:

"You'll fuckin find that I'm a good patient. If you make a fuckin recommendation for my health I will fuckin-A follow it through to the fuckin completion."

He was scheduled for a follow-up appointment.

It will be f----n interesting to see if he has a f----n new favorite word for his next f----n visit.

TWENTY-SIX: CUSTODIAL SPECIALISTS

Isn't it crazy how many medical subspecialists have formed? There's a large orthopedic group in town that has a specialist for most every body part. If you ask the "knee guy" a question about your shoulder he/she will let you know that you'll need to set up an appointment with the "shoulder specialist."

Luckily, they haven't separated the sides of the body yet. In other words, I'm happy that the knee specialist will still evaluate both the right and left knee if needed.

Recently I saw a 54 y/o male who was working at an adult retirement community. It was good to see that medicine isn't alone in their quest for specialists.

Patient: I need work restrictions. I have a bad back. I'm a custodian at the retirement community across the street and pretty much have to do it all.

Me: Do you have to lift and repair things?

Patient: No, that falls under the maintenance department.

Me: Do you have to clean up?

Patient: No, that's the housekeeping department.

Me: Painting?

Patient: No, we have painters.

Me: Clean the floors?

Patient: No, we have floor techs.

Me: What do you do?

Patient: I take out the trash.

Me: All day?

Patient: All day, except for when I'm on a break.

I was just glad he didn't refer to himself as a "trash taker-outer except when on break specialist."

TWENTY-SEVEN: TWO ED'S; JOKESTERS 'TIL THE END

My Dad and my Uncle were both named Ed. Both were jokesters even when they were old and near death.

The ability to retain their sense of humor, even when physically ill, was another wonderful life lesson they bestowed upon their families.

My Dad was quite ill before he died but had a couple of favorite answers to my questions. The answers were simple but yet would always bring a smile to his face. I still can hear him answering whenever I ask the same questions to my patients.

Me: How do you feel Dad?

Dad: With my hands, son, with my hands.

Me: Can you hear OK?

Dad: What?

Me: Can you…oh, not again…you got me.

My Uncle Ed's health was also very poor before he died from complications of lymphoma. My Aunt Barbara told me a story that occurred just before he died. He had been poorly responsive and was considered to be in critical condition. When he aroused once he called my Aunt over to his side.

Uncle Ed: Barbara, come here for a second.

Barbara: Yes Ed, I'm here (She then goes on to tell how she bent down close to him and was expecting him to whisper sweet nothings about the long life they had shared together).

Uncle Ed: Your breath is terrible (smiling)...did you brush your teeth today?

TWENTY-EIGHT: ON-OFF SURPRISE

My Dad had Parkinson's disease for many years.

In the later stages of his illness he had a condition called on-off syndrome.

Basically, there were times when he was mobile and other times when he was completely immobile.

Initially he could predict the times that he would "turn on" and be able to move (usually based on the timing of his medication).

However, as his disease progressed, it became more unpredictable.

When he could move, he often had choreic (involuntary muscular twitching of the limb or facial muscles) movements, due to a peak of dopamine in the central nervous system.

He preferred to move and have choreic movements over the alternative; being unable to move at all (being stiff and immobile).

Other consequences of his disease as it progressed were cognitive and impulse control issues.

This combination often yielded many memorable events.

Basically, whenever he would turn on he would try to "escape." He had places to go and people to see.

Many times he would escape while my Mom was taking a nap or had fallen asleep watching TV.

Obviously she would panic when she would wake from a nap and find he was gone.

Sometimes he would freeze close to their home and was easily found.

Other times he could be miles away, and would be brought home by friends, neighbors or the local police.

Once he had a covert outing that escaped detection. In other words he was able to get to his destination and back without freezing or getting caught.

We only discovered this outing when my brother was out on a date.

He and his girlfriend went to rent a video.

The clerk noted that he had an overdue video and had accumulated a significant late charge.

My brother was surprised. "What movie is overdue?" he asked.

The store clerk told him. It was an X-rated movie.

"Oh" he said, "that must be my father. I gave him one of my membership cards."

Sure enough, the video was in the top drawer of my fathers' dresser, hidden under some T-shirts.

We never told my mother about it.

She already had more than her fair share of on-off surprises.

TWENTY-NINE: SIMILAR THOUGHTS

I'm not sure why I considered my sister to be my archenemy growing up. I was the youngest child in my family. She was the sibling closest in age.

I was a real pest toward her. I got away with almost everything. I perfected having an innocent look on my face in the midst of whatever chaos I had engineered. She usually took the brunt of the punishment handed out by my mother whenever we were caught in the midst of a disagreement.

I have apologized multiple times for my past behavior.

Surprisingly, we ended up having many similarities in our lives.

We're both doctors, married and have two children.

We even think a lot alike.

I came across some thoughts that we jotted down to ourselves after my father had died. Mine was in the form of a letter to my father. Eva's was also in a letter format. I don't remember how we decided to share the letters with each other but it was uncanny to see some of our similar thoughts. I have included them below (mine first, followed by my sister):

Dear Dad,

You had been sick for so long it's hard to remember a time that you weren't...but there was a time...and it's great to remember what a wonderful life you had...

You loved life and so many things over the years:

-it was obvious by your actions that you loved Mom for over 46 years, your children, family and friends

It also appeared to me that you loved:

-Roller coasters, especially the "Cyclone" at Coney Island

-Eggs over easy with extra crisp bacon

-Taking a tablespoon of peanut butter and eating it like a lollipop

-Telling jokes and sometimes laughing so hard that you could barely get to the punch line

-Having your hair slicked back

-Dancing, especially the jitterbug

-Chopped steak, covered to the max with ketchup

-The carvel ice-cream sandwiches called "flying saucers"

-Barbecues

-Drinking beer out of the big glass that was shaped like an hour-glass

-McDonald's hamburgers and vanilla shakes

-Cars, especially your 1966 red mustang convertible

-All animals, especially dogs

-Gadgets-mechanical things-especially anything that you could take apart and improve somehow with your own personal touches

-Radio controlled airplanes-you loved building the airplanes from scratch, flying them and then re-building and modifying them for the next flight

-Model trains

-Water skiing

-Motor homes

& body surfacing in the ocean

You were always up to something. You were always working on things to patent. I remember you buying the first cars for Jack and Eva in a junkyard and totally rebuilding them in our garage until late at night and doing the entire engine and body work by yourself. I remember how excited we would be when you would arrive home from traveling for business with some treats for everyone.

I know at times you were frustrated and disappointed in the way things worked out physically and career wise, but you were an excellent father. You taught of life lessons by example. It was always wonderful when we would play catch, shoot baskets or play any other sports. You never raised your voice unless we did something that was dangerous to others or ourselves. You and Mom always made it a priority to be there for events. I knew you would both be sitting in the stands before any sporting event started, often there before I had arrived on the team bus. You put your family first, at times sacrificing things you may have wanted. One of your favorite cars besides your Mustang was your Chevy Monte Carlo. I know you loved it but didn't seem to mind when Ed and Jack hi-jacked it for college and returned it to you with about 100,000 miles on it.

You encouraged us all to enjoy life and to never give up or run away from our problems. You always treated others with respect, no matter their status in life. You were never afraid to do the dirty work. "Someone has to clean the toilets," you would say. You never harbored grudges. You showed us the importance of a good sense of humor. You showed us how wonderful it is to have life-long friends.

A disease is not simply a disorder of bodily function or structures-it has far reaching effects on the whole person. Disease can change relationships, alter priorities, challenge faith, raise fears and crush dreams. At times your disease did all of the above. You put up a good fight. You should be proud of the legacy that you have left behind. Despite your struggle for over thirty years with Parkinson's disease, I'm sure you would be the first to say that it was a wonderful life.

Love, Bill

My Dad had been sick for so long, it's hard to remember him as a younger man. His Parkinson's disease made him physically old before his time. It didn't seem to have the same effect on his psyche. Despite his many physical hardships and his waffling cognition, he always maintained a youthful spirit and a naïve, almost untarnished optimism. Even his delusions were consistent with this. In some ways he was the luckiest man alive. He had a devoted wife with him thru thick and thin. He thought he won the publishers clearinghouse sweepstakes numerous times and that he recently acquired ownership of his own airlines.

I remember him as a tinkerer and an inventor who always had a handful of ideas ready to make his fortune. He could take anything apart…and before his illness was too advanced, he could even put some of them back together. He loved anything to do with flying, he loved the ocean, and he loved to dance. He never gave up his hope of buying and living in a motor home. He would have been very happy touring the country in that way. He wasn't beyond a practical joke or two and he had a great sense of humor.

The on-off phenomena of Parkinson's was quite a challenge for him, and maybe more so for Mom, who had to answer to the rescue squad every time Dad felt mobile enough to wander off and get frozen at the video store, the grocery store or elsewhere. I don't mean to focus on the illness, but he was sick more of my life than he was healthy. From late adolescence, his illness was a central part of our family.

My kids are here today, Emma and Wally. They love their Poppie. They could always relate to his struggles to walk and talk and be independent in the world. His struggles were similar to their own. They want him to have love and comfort. I do too. They want to know that his family loves him and they want to know that God will take care of him. I think all those things are true.

With his passing our family story enters into a new chapter. I'm not sure what it will be about. I hope it is about Mom beginning to live again in ways she has put on hold for so long. I hope it is about my brother's and me reconnecting in new ways as adults and our children being able to share in the sense of a large and expanding family. Life in our family has been challenging. Dad's illness has affected us all in ways I can only begin to understand. I pray that God will see fit to care for Dad's youthful spirit in a way that allows him to run and jump and fly and pray while he looks down at his family making the best of their lives, their good fortunes and their challenges.

Love, Eva

My sister lives in California with her family.

We don't get to see each other very often.

She has a great partner.

Her children seem happy and are doing well.

I couldn't be happier or more proud of my sister.

She's the same sister I spent years trying to emotionally torture when we were young.

THIRTY: TOTAL DORK OR A GOOD LUCK CHARM?

When I was younger I played most sports. However, I played very little volleyball, never on a school team and didn't know the official rules other than only being allowed to have three hits on a side.

My son has played on his middle school volleyball team for the last couple of years. During the season this year his coach asked me to be a line judge for a game. He gave me a ten second instruction while handing me two flags:

1. Ball hits the line at any point is considered in.
2. When ball is in, arms and flags are in a down position.
3. When ball is out, arms and flags are in an up position.
4. Server must hit the ball before stepping on or crossing the service line.

"Got it?" he asked. "Got it," I replied.

I assumed my position, the whole time silently chanting to myself, ball in, arms down, ball out, arms up.

I thought the game went pretty well. My wife said afterwards that I was a little "twitchy" but that's not out of the ordinary for me. My son's team won the game.

I drove my son home from the game.

"Why were you a line judge?" he asked.

"Because your coach asked me," I replied.

"Well…you looked like a total dork out there," he continued, "You could have just said no."

"Why thanks for the compliment," I said, trying not to show him my true feelings.

My wife and I laughed about it later that night.

Much to my sons' disappointment, his coach continued to ask me to be a line judge. They didn't lose another game. They were 1-4 when I judged the first game and they finished the regular season at 4-4. I think the coach thought I was sort of a good luck charm. As my confidence grew in my position, the confidence in my calls also improved. By the last game I was throwing my flags up or down with the best in the business…if I do say so myself.

To my sons' credit, he finally gave me some good feedback. He told me that during one of the games another player named Luis turned to him and said "it's cool how your Dad seems to get so into the games."

It felt good to be cool again.

Thanks Luis!!

THIRTY-ONE: SPEAKING OF NOT KNOWING THE RULES

I've enjoyed coaching many youth sports over the years. Probably one of the most enjoyable coaching experiences was for a sport I was not prepared to coach in the first place. My son was signed up to play flag football through the YMCA in the 8-9 y/o division. When I took him to the first practice the director of youth sports asked if I would volunteer to coach, since he didn't have a coach for my son's team. He knew me from coaching other sports. I let him know that I had never coached flag football before and he assured me that he would get me a copy of the rules. I volunteered.

We had three practices before the first game. Most of the time was spent having fun and trying to teach a few basics. We even worked on a few running plays. I didn't have a kid on the team that could throw a football more than about 10 yards.

I was never given the rules.

We showed up early for the first game. There was another game in progress on the field. The kids were calling their own plays, players were being sent in motion, long pass plays were being completed and defensive signals were shouted out and line shifts would occur. It was an exciting game to watch. I finally saw someone I knew and asked what age division was playing.

"8-9 year-olds" was the reply.

I knew we were in big trouble.

We lost the first game 49-6. We scored a touchdown on the last play of the game but missed the extra point. I learned the rules quickly. For example, when you were within 5 yards of the first down marker you were in what was called the no-run zone. In other words, you had to pass the ball. As already noted, my kids couldn't throw the ball. We didn't get any first downs for the first game. My son ran about 69 yards on the last play of the game for our only score.

But we had fun, usually. I made sure of it. Each week we got a little better. Each week I made sure the kids rotated to another position. Every kid got to play quarterback. I got a complete set of rules and quickly memorized them. I called the youth sports director and got great tips on how to play defense. I went to the local library and checked out some books. I even found a flag football website on the internet.

One night I woke up from a deep sleep with an epiphany…the shovel pass. We started to utilize a shovel pass to a back or a receiver, out of the shot gun formation, whenever we needed to complete a pass. It worked pretty well. We could finally actually do something when in the no run zone.

We finished the regular season 0-8. All teams got to play in the playoffs. Obviously we were the 8th seed. When we beat the #1 seed we all felt like we had won the NFL championship. We won two of the last three games and finished as the second place team, officially, for the season. I still get a smile on my face whenever I think about that team, as does my son. Hopefully, the other players do as well.

I went on to coach four more seasons of flag football. We had some great teams. One season I know we could have gone undefeated but I always insisted on a few things. Every kid rotated through all positions. Every kid got to play at least one half of every game. Every kid got to play quarterback for at least half a game during the season. The parents of the kids were told this as well in case they wanted to change their child to a different team

When coaching youth sports it's easy, at times, to get caught up "in the moment." All of us have to tendency to think "win at all costs." Whenever I would start to think that way my wife could always bring me back with two reminders:

1. They're just kids, let them have fun.
2. Kids know how to have fun playing sports. It's usually the grown-ups who screw things up.

THIRTY-TWO: SPEAKING ABOUT LOSING

Have you ever been to a Cub Scout sponsored "pinewood derby car race?"

If not, read on. It will give you a little heads-up as to what to expect.

Basically it's a race with a miniature car the kids are supposed to make. The Scouts are given a box containing a small block of wood and some wheels. The rest is up to the scout's imagination.

My son was six. I was a den leader but it was my first Pinewood Derby.

My son drew how he wanted the car to be shaped on the block of wood. I used a jig- saw to cut it. He did the rest. He sanded and painted it, positioned the wheels and placed some racing stickers on the sides. He even glued on his favorite Lego man with a crash helmet as the driver. It was a car that any six y/o would have been proud to make.

We arrived early for the event. It took place in the elementary school cafeteria. A two-lane track was set up and looked pretty cool. The room was a bustle of activity.

Everywhere around the room dads, and sometimes even the scouts, were huddled over the cars. Most of the dads had tackle boxes that housed all their pinewood car paraphernalia. The most important item appeared to be what looked like a post office scale.

"Why did folks have a scale?" I thought to myself.

"Oh, no one told you about the weight of your child's car?" said one of the dads who had probably seen me looking at a scale with a confused expression.

"No" I replied.

He then went on to explain the car could be up to 5 ounces in weight and the heavier cars were always the fastest.

I sat there watching the other dads use hot glue guns to attach small weights to the undersurface of the cars and immediately felt like a failure as a father. They would apply one weight, weigh the car, apply another if needed, etc, etc.

My son was off to the side rolling his car on a flat table. He looked happy. He was proud of his car. It looked cool. I sat there with him trying to hide my concern.

The Cub Master sat up front with an official scale. Prior to the race the kids would hand their car over for the official weigh in. The weights would then be entered on a piece of recording paper.

4.84 Ounces, he would announce.

Amazing, awesome and other spoken adjectives followed.

4.96 Ounces.

Even more glowing adjectives followed.

And so forth and so on.

1.1 Ounces.

Snickers and mild laughter was heard.

It was my son's car.

The race results were as expected. It was a double elimination event. My son's car didn't have enough speed on either race to even get to the bottom of the track. He was quickly eliminated.

The car that won was a slick, aerodynamic looking masterpiece that weighed approx 4.99 Ounces. The father who made the car…I mean the scout who owned the car was very proud.

The ride home was quiet. I didn't know what to say. Finally I came up with an idea.

"Hey Tommy, guess what?"

"What Dad?"

"Of all the cars there tonight, in a few days, I bet most folks will only remember two cars…the fastest and the slowest."

"That's right; we probably have the slowest car in the history of Cub Scouts."

We laughed.

Adults need to remember the basics needed to win the pinewood derby car race for your child: a scale, a glue gun, and perhaps, more importantly, to even make the car for your child.

To my bitter disappointment he decided not to continue with scouts the next year.

He wanted to spend more time doing other things, especially sports.

Oh darn (#1).

THIRTY-THREE: OH DARN #2

When my daughter was younger she did gymnastics for about two years.

The training center was a converted warehouse.

I'll admit that I had no gymnastics background whatsoever. I would watch the Olympics every four years. I knew very little about the sport.

The "parent room" was an old storage room. It was a medium sized room with a large picture window looking down on the work out floor.

You could see the entire floor if you arrived early and were lucky enough to get one of the incredibly uncomfortable metal chairs in the front row.

Otherwise you would have to stand to see anything. This was the only place parents were allowed. The room was always hot and there was always a strong smell of competing colognes and perfumes in the air. The room had very little ventilation.

Even when I had something to read it was always more interesting to eavesdrop on other peoples' conversations. Most dealt with important world issues such as home renovations, hair style and color, good manicure locations and how things were going with their gardeners and housekeepers.

Most of the gymnasts, especially the older girls, looked so unhappy. Some looked down right miserable.

Most of them had bandages and ace wraps over various parts of their bodies to help stabilize injuries.

Most were incredibly thin.

The coaches seemed to mainly offer criticism, even after it appeared to me that some amazing gymnastic move had just taken place.

My wife and I took turns taking our daughter.

We always felt like Gilligan setting out for a three hour tour.

One day our daughter announced she wanted to do other sports like her brother, not just concentrate on one sport. We agreed it was a good idea but also tried to look neutral.

My wife and I spent time alone "high-fiving" each other that evening.

Oh Darn #2.

THIRTY-FOUR: SWIM TEAM PRACTICE: ANOTHER FORM OF CHILD ABUSE

As a family we have our usual assortment of arguments, disagreements, and hurt feelings. For the most part, we have always been able to work things out.

Swim team practice, however, presented itself as sort of an unexpected challenge. Without a doubt it was about the maddest my wife and I had ever seen our kids.

It started off with the best of intentions. My kids love to swim. My wife and I decided that it would be good exercise to have the kids join the YMCA swim team for the summer. My son was eleven and my daughter nine at the time.

The coach seemed nice. He let us know that he was an ex-Marine and was still a reservist. I suppose we should have taken that as a hint as to what would follow. We decided to watch the whole practice.

Although Tom and Ellie were new to the team, they were expected to go through the regular practice. Many of the other kids on the team had already been swimming for months.

I stopped counting laps when the total reached about a mile in distance. Between most sets, my son would barely acknowledge our existence but we could see that he was visibly upset. My daughter, between sets, would look at us with a confused, bewildered expression as if wanting to know why we were punishing her.

To their credit, they both completed the first practice.

No words were spoken as they grabbed their stuff and we walked to the car. No words whatsoever were spoken for most of the drive home. Finally, my son broke the silence.

"Has a kid ever drowned at swim practice?"

"I don't know...I don't think so" was the only reply I could think of at the time.

"Remember the other night when you told us cocaine was bad for you because it can elevate your heart rate?"

"Yes, I remember."

"Swim practice does the same thing as cocaine. Why don't you just start having us take cocaine?"

Very little was said for the rest of the evening. Not surprisingly, both went to bed early that night and slept late the next morning.

The next day we opted to come up with a compromise. Stick it out for at least two weeks and then we'll re-evaluate.

They did.

They both improved quickly. As their endurance improved their anger abated somewhat but they didn't show any signs of wanting the swim team to be a long term venture.

I don't think my son would ever accept wearing a swim cap and a Speedo to improve his speed to a competitive level. He was also too young to notice that all the girls on the team were pretty.

Also, although my daughter loves to exercise, it was clear that swimming over a mile a day would never become a preferred aerobic activity.

Since the pool was outside practice would occasionally be cancelled or shortened due to lightning. This natural occurrence always made for a much better day mood wise. I think the kids took it upon themselves to watch closely for any signs of lightning and to report it at once.

They stopped swimming on the swim team after the summer. School was getting ready to start and other "more enjoyable" activities would begin.

Although the swim team never became a long term commitment it did highlight some important life lessons. Life lessons, however, that only a parent could appreciate.

I know my kids thought of swim practice as a form of child abuse.

But I also know they were very thankful that neither of them drowned in the process!

THIRTY-FIVE: LIFE LESSONS OF JV BASKETBALL

When I was 15 years old I tried out for my high school JV basketball team. It was definitely an awkward time in my life. I was a late bloomer. Many of the other guys were more physically developed. I was a string bean. I was almost 6 foot tall but only weighed about 150 pounds. My sister said she always felt like my uniform was going to fall off whenever I would run up and down the court.

I made the team. After the first practice Coach Spillett called me over to the side to let me know I was the 13th man on a team with 13 players. He wanted to make sure I was OK with the fact that I wouldn't be playing much during the games.

"Are you kidding?" I thought. I was just happy to have made the team.

I sat at the end of the bench for our first game. We were losing by 20 points and there were only about two minutes left in the game when Coach put me in. I did the only thing I knew I could do. I hustled. I got a couple of rebounds and dove for a couple of loose balls. I did not score any points. We lost the game by 18 points.

Coach Biaetti, the Varsity Coach, was watching the game. I learned later that he thought it was great that I was continuing to hustle even though we were losing by so many points. He asked the JV coach to play me earlier in the next game.

I assumed my position for the second game at the end of the bench. Coach called my name to enter the game during the 1st quarter. My team mates had no idea what was going on. I played most of the game before fouling out. I scored 8 points and had 11 rebounds. We lost the game.

I started every game for the rest of the year.

I received the most improved and most valuable player of the year award for our team that year.

1St life lesson: Hustle and sometimes good things will happen.

We had a terrible team. Actually, I should probably just say we weren't as good as the other teams we played.

Our high school mascot was "The Pelicans."

We were the Pelham Pelicans...no kidding! It's a mascot that definitely did not strike fear in the eyes of any of our opponents. Pelicans are beautiful birds but always appear to be slow and sort of dopey.

Woodlands, a school in our league, had a great team. They crushed us the first time we played for the year. The players, and even their students in the crowd, were making a lot of comments about how bad we were as a team.

The players on our team decided to walk off the court after the game without shaking their hands.

Coach Spillett came in the locker room and was furious. He told us that he had never been more ashamed of a team. He went on to say he wasn't ashamed of how we played but by our lack of sportsmanship in losing. He reminded us that in life we will always come across people who may have more skill or talent in a particular area. He encouraged us to focus our anger and energies from losing on improving as individuals and as a team. He told us to always walk away from a competition proud to have put forth your best effort. He advised us to always shake the hands of the opposing players, win or lose.

After we showered and dressed, our team waited outside the other team locker room and shook hands with them. Their players were surprised.

We played them again later in the year and still lost. The game however was much closer. It was actually tied until the 4th quarter. We lost by only 6 points.

2nd life lesson: Compete to the best of your ability but always acknowledge your opponent, win or lose.

After the first 14 games we were 0-14. We only had one game left. I was told students were betting around the school on if we would win or lose our last game for the season.

We won. We ended the season 1-14. By winning the last game, however, we felt as if we had won the NBA championship.

3rd life lesson: Stick to the fight when you are hardest hit; it's when things look worst that you must not quit.

I went on to play two more years of high school basketball. I gained almost 35 pounds during the summer between my sophomore and junior year of high school and grew another three inches.

I made the all-league team my senior year.

I played three years at the University of Virginia.

I played on some great teams but many of my favorite sport memories are of my 1-14 high school JV basketball team.

The life lessons have remained with me.

* Hustle and sometimes good things will happen.

* Compete to the best of your ability but always acknowledge your opponent, win or lose.

* Stick to the fight when you are hardest hit; it's when things look worst that you must not quit.

THIRTY-SIX: THREE HARD EARNED POINTS

My son loves all sports.

Basketball is definitely one of his favorites

He has played through the YMCA and was on his school's 6th grade team last year.

He made the 7th/8th grade team this past year.

Eleven boys made the team from the almost 100 kids who tried out.

Only two seventh graders made the team; Tom and another boy named Kevin.

His coach told him he would probably not play in games at all. He told him to talk to his parents to make sure it would be alright.

My son was so shocked to have made the team he wasn't even sure what to tell us.

My wife sent an e-mail to the coach the next day:

"Tom was so shocked to have made the team in any capacity yesterday that he wasn't able to process all the information you gave him beyond he needs to show up for practice but won't be playing in the games. Could you touch base with us when possible? Thanks."

Later in the day he replied:

"I am so happy to have Tom on the team. He is such a good kid and just pleasant to be around. He will be coming to practice everyday, working with the team, learning the plays, going through drills and of course conditioning. He will have the capacity to play in a game if I feel he is ready to go against the big boys. He is not the towel boy or the water boy in any capacity. He is 100% part of the team, just not playing in the games yet. This will definitely help him for next year. He will know the plays as well as the expectations that we will have for the players. It will be a long and tough season and we are going to be tough on him to try and get him to be successful."

My wife replied the next day:

"This is fabulous. Thank you so much for the time and energy you are giving him. He has verbalized that he wants to play on the team next year and is planning on using this opportunity to learn more and hone his skills on the big court against the big guys. Our driveway hoop and the kids with the YMCA sports don't really give him the competition he needs. He will work his heart out for you and loves to play.

Bill and I appreciate how meaningful this experience can be for him. We think this is a perfect chance for him to work through some of his current social and developmental "awkwardness" in a less pressured kind of way. It is hard for him to feel like he fits in right now. None of his academic peers are interested in sports and many of the sports oriented kids have a "swagger" that he isn't ready to challenge. As you have sensed, he is a really intense kid and we know as he grows into himself he has the potential to be a big part of any team. If you ever need a laugh, we have some really funny stories of how his intensity has kept us on our toes!

Again, thank you for everything you are doing for my kid and all the others that you coach."

When he initially approached me about being on the team with the chance he might not play at all I said "that's totally cool-it's sort of like going to college and being red shirted. It gives you a year to grow and develop without the pressure of having to play in a game yet."

He bought into the whole idea.

He worked his butt off.

He had practice every morning during the week from 6:50 AM until 9:25 AM. School started at 9:30 AM.

Even on game days they would practice from 8 AM until 9:25 AM.

As the season went on he got some playing time.

It was usually at the end of a game.

The first time he had a "deer in the head lights look about him."

His confidence improved throughout the season.

He got some rebounds during some games and made some nice passes.

He even took a few shots.

None went in.

His team made the championship game of the county tournament.

It was the last game of the season.

His team was down by about 16 points with two minutes to go.

Tom went into the game.

With 1 minute and 16 seconds left in the game he got a pass from a teammate under the basket.

He went up strong. The ball went in and he was fouled. He went to the free throw line and sank the free throw.

His team mates all stood and cheered. Some of the bigger guys patted him on his head.

They all knew it was his first points of the season.

They lost by 14 points, but I'm pretty sure he went to sleep with a big smile on his face after the last game.

Those were three hard earned points.

THIRTY-SEVEN: RESPECT MUST BE EARNED

What follows is an editorial I wrote for our local newspaper a few years ago:

I saw a recent interview during halftime of a game on television with a player I hope remains with the Orlando Magic. He stated that he perceives a lack of respect from the people of Orlando. It seems to me this was a concern of another superstar player who left our team two years ago. Although he moved out west, many fans all around town continue to wear his endorsed $100 sneakers and $50 jerseys and drink "his" soda.

Respect should always be earned, not expected. Most people respect individuals, no matter their position or income level, who are caring, honest, hard-working and who help others.

When fans spend about $200 for their family of four to attend a home game (perhaps their only game of the year), it's not too much to expect an athlete making $6 million a year (or about 16,500 a day, or about $73,000 a game if the athlete plays all 82 games a year) to turn in a hard-working or all-out effort most every day, both on and off the court. Fans get disappointed if they perceive a lack of commitment, effort or interest in their team, just as players expect an amount of perfection from the contractors who build their 25,000 square-foot, million dollar homes, the performance of their $60,000 cars and the team physicians who are consulted about their injuries.

Fans go to work every day with ailments such as reflux, tendonitis, ingrown toenails and sprained ankles, and remain supportive of these players when the players are visibly and vocally supportive of the team when they are unable to play.

I believe the superstar interviewed has done many things to earn our respect and that the city has embraced him as our franchise player. If he does decide to take his basketball talents elsewhere next year, I hope he won't insult us again by using a "lack of respect" as his reason to leave.

THIRTY-EIGHT: THE BUCKING BRONCO

We always look forward to family vacations.

We try to rotate trips and destinations based on both our individual and collective interests. My daughter loves horses so we planned a trip last year to a working ranch in North Carolina. My wife made all the arrangements, including scheduling us for a three hour horseback ride through the national forest.

I've never been a huge fan of horseback riding. Actually, the one experience I had as a teenager was so painful I had not ridden since. It seemed that my butt was always going down whenever the saddle was going up.

I couldn't understand why I was forced to wear a "cup" to play little league baseball but a protective "cup" was not on the list of required clothing for a horseback ride.

We arrived at the stable. What follows is my fabricated version of the events. I will then add what I think would be my daughter's version, a probably more actual account of the day.

My version: The workers (the stable hands) brought all the horses out of the stable. Immediately I couldn't help but notice one of the horses was huge, bigger than any of the rest. It appeared to me he was a "bucking bronco," possibly a horse just obtained that needed to be broken. His name "Cody" didn't do justice to his massive size. Cody spent the whole time giving me the evil eye. He also decided to take a huge, massive dump while we were waiting.

Best of all, I was informed I would be riding the bucking bronco. I was just glad to have spared my family members from having to risk their lives.

He allowed me to cautiously mount his saddle after flashing his teeth and letting out a loud, threatening, snorting type of sound.

We then all set off on a trail ride. The trail guide, my wife, son and daughter on four little well behaved horses followed closely by me, on the wild eyed beast.

Shortly into the ride a wild turkey went flying out of the brush. Immediately, all the horses got spooked and took off in a gallop that must have lasted for 15 seconds or more. Finally, using all my strength, I was able to rein my horse in and get control of what could have been a tragic situation. Once I got control of my horse, and the situation, all the other horses seemed to fall back into line.

It was a good thing I was around. I'm sure everyone felt the same way.

We still had over two hours left on the ride. We spent the rest of the time walking through the trail and I resisted all attempts and requests from the other riders to trot or canter.

I figured we all had weathered enough for the day. I also tried to make sure none of the other horses poked into mine, so as to not set off the dreaded "chain reaction" in which all the horses might start to run wild and buck their rider.

Thanks to my attempts at keeping the horses and all the other riders controlled, we arrived safely back at the stable.

My only battle wound for the day was a sore butt.

My daughter's version: We had fun but my Dad was a total "Nancy-boy." The only horse smaller or older looking than his was Mom's. Her horse was called "Little Joe." Dad's horse was named "Cody." He was a cute little horse.

Yes, Cody did take a dump prior to the ride, as did all the other horses.

We set out on the trail ride. My horse went off to the side to pee and a wild turkey that was in the brush went running out. All the horses got spooked for four or five seconds. My horse was the most scared due to being the closest to the turkey.

The look on Dad's face was funny. He was almost totally pale. He could barely speak.

Unfortunately, that one event pretty much did him in for the day. He was nervous to go on the trail ride in the first place. Before we went he kept talking about what an awful experience he had when riding as a young teenager.

Since we were together we needed to all agree to trot or canter. Dad had regained a little color in his face but wouldn't agree. He also wanted to make sure that none of our horses got too close to his horse. He kept mumbling something about not wanting to start a chain reaction. I wasn't sure what he was talking about but it was good to see that he could talk again.

We walked the entire way.

It was fun but it could have been more exciting to trot for awhile. It was also a little annoying when we had to move to the side to let a group of young children come trotting past us on their trail ride.

Once back at the stable, and off his horse, Dad started to talk about what a great time was had by all.

He started talking about what a wild adventure it had been...Yawn.

He also started talking about the bucking bronco and reliving the wild turkey episode.

He couldn't stop taking about his sore butt.

Whatever...it was fun though...we had some great laughs.

I just think we'll all have to do our best to keep Dad from going on another horse ride with us in the future.

Maybe we can drop him off at a local mall to ride a kid's mechanical horse for a quarter.

I sure some tall-tales would follow that adventure as well.

THIRTY-NINE: NANCY BOY #2, #3 AND #4

I'm coming clean so I might as well get it all out.

Nancy boy #2:

I never went fishing growing up. Come to think of it, I haven't eaten a lot of fish over the course of my life except for tuna fish and fish sticks. My wife always calls me a "city boy."

My wife's Dad loves to fish. He took us fishing years ago with some other members of the family. I caught a fish. When I went to remove the fish from the hook I instinctively grabbed a towel first so that I wouldn't need to actually touch the fish. All the other men on board, including my father in law, thought it was pretty amusing. Even some of the women laughed at me. My wife just smirked.

Nancy boy #2:

We've always loved to go on walks through some of the parks nearby. On this particular day I was walking a step or two ahead of everyone else. Out of the corner of my eye I saw a snake move across the side of the trail. My wife says she has never seen me move quicker. I ran about twenty feet at full speed before remembering I was with my family and was their "protector."

I felt pretty wimpy when I finally stopped, turned around and saw my wife standing there holding our dog by a leash and pushing our two kids in a stroller.

"Yes," she confirmed, "it was a ferocious looking black garden snake!" She had the same smirk on her face again.

Nancy boy #3:

And finally, my most consistent and longest lasting Nancy "boy-ism." I'm pretty sure I watched Jaws too frequently when I was a young boy. I've never been comfortable swimming in the ocean. Even though I love being at the ocean I can't get the Jaws music out of my head whenever swimming. Not only that, I hate the fact that I might step on a crab that I can't see.

My kids love to swim in the ocean. It wasn't until they were older when they finally asked why I always seem to be treading water and constantly scanning the horizon when swimming in the ocean. I finally had to tell them that I hate walking on the ocean floor because of crabs and that I'm on alert for shark fins at all times.

Yep, you got it...their smirks look just like my wife's!

FORTY: AN OBVIOUS QUESTION

I've had two "professional" massages.

My wife gave me a gift certificate for a spa day, which included a massage, for Father's Day one year.

It sounded like a great idea at first. However, as the date neared, the more nervous I felt.

Would I really be naked except for a towel?

What about the therapist?

If it was a woman I was concerned about the way I look with my clothes off. I've got hair EVERYWHERE and some "love handles."

Also, what if it felt too good? Would I be embarrassed if something started to "awaken" under my towel?

What if it was a guy?

Would I really feel comfortable with a guy giving me a massage?

It ended up being a woman. She was very professional and obviously, there was nothing sexual about the experience. I had spent a lot of time worrying about nothing.

My wife and I had a "couples massage" more recently. We each had our own masseuse and were on separate tables. I was relaxed. It was amazing. Unfortunately, it seemed like the quickest hour of my life.

I'd definitely do it again. It's just too expensive to make it part of a routine.

I've had two pedicures in my life.

I had the first on the same spa day as my first massage.

I pretty much had the same outcome. I was so nervous about someone working on my feet that I didn't really enjoy it.

I recently went for a second pedicure due to an ingrown toenail.

It was great. My big toe got a new lease on life almost immediately.

Unfortunately I felt like a "Nancy boy" again when I ran into a female co-worker who had come to the same nail salon.

She recognized me even though I had on dark sun glasses, a baseball hat and tried to avoid all eye contact.

It would be great if they had some male only pedicure spots.

So I'm two for two. I enjoy BOTH massages and pedicures.

It brings up an obvious question:

Does it mean I've got metro sexual potential?

Only time will tell.

FORTY-ONE: THE CABIN STEWARD

Quick question: What do you call the person who graduated in the bottom of his medical school class?

Answer: Doctor.

Actually, I did very well in medical school. It still doesn't keep me from being a goof ball at times, however.

Another recent vacation for our family was a cruise. We were joined by my mother and a friend of hers, as well as by my wife's mother and brother.

Trying to be courteous and respectful I introduced myself to our cabin steward when we arrived to our state room (actually an approximate 10 x 10 room with two sets of bunk beds and a small bathroom).

I was sure that he introduced himself to me as "Stuart."

I then proceeded to spend the next seven days calling him Stuart.

"Have a good day Stuart, we will be out of our room now Stuart, we need more toilet paper Stuart, thanks so much for the towels Stuart."

When we were getting ready to leave I was working on the tips for the crew. My brother in law was in the next cabin. He had the same cabin steward. He had the name Javier on one of the envelopes. I asked, "Who is Javier?"

"Our cabin steward," he replied.

"Oh," I responded, "I've just spent the week calling our cabin steward Stuart."

Javier, I suspect, figured I was just another condescending American. He probably thought I spent the week on the cruise saying things such as "thank you waiter, appreciate it bartender, good work engine crew man, nice show entertainment staff."

As usual, I came clean with my wife and kids. They couldn't stop laughing.

My wife says she thought, all along, that it was an odd name for someone of his ethnicity.

She occasionally forgets about my goof ball tendencies, as well as my hearing loss. I tried to rebuke the laughter from my kids by letting them know that people call me "Doctor" all day at the office.

They countered by requesting that I not change their names to kid #1 and kid #2, if possible.

FORTY-TWO: COME ON, JUST SNAP OUT OF IT

I love cruises.

Maybe it's an inherited trait.

My parents loved cruises.

I have a brother that's been on over 60 cruises.

The food and entertainment are great and its fun stopping at different destinations.

The price is also great, compared to most other family vacations.

We've gone on three cruises as a family.

We always get a cabin near the bottom of the ship and without a window because it's less expensive.

We do a ton of walking since the dining facilities, pools, etc are all on the top levels of the ship.

We get a good work out walking up and down the steps.

The only problem is my son gets sea sick.

He's gotten motion sickness for years.

He throws up on most every descent whenever we fly.

He throws up on most every LONG car ride.

We've tried every possible treatment over the years.

Nothing has worked consistently.

Our first family cruise was a disaster.

Luckily it was only a three day cruise.

He spent most of the time feeling like crap.

We waited a few years before trying another.

Things went better.

It was a brand new ship; almost twice the size of most ships and the sea was calm.

We thought we had "turned the corner."

We signed up for another.

We went with some of our extended family members.

It was a seven day cruise.

It was a great deal (usually high on my list of priorities).

The ship was an older ship (half the size of the most previous ship we had been on).

The sea was rough.

For dinner we requested to have a table large enough to seat everyone in our party.

Our only other request was to have a table in the middle of the room, AWAY from the windows.

Our assigned table was up against a huge picture window looking out at the ocean.

My son tried to "hang in there" for as long as possible for our first meal at sea.

He excused himself to go back to our room.

My wife went with him.

She gave me a look that only husbands could appreciate.

I stayed for the remainder of the two hour, four course meal.

When we left the dining room there was a large section of the hallway roped off. One stairwell was also roped off.

It appeared that someone had vomited everywhere.

I heard my son's moans from outside the room door.

My wife was putting a cool wash cloth on his head.

She confirmed that he had vomited in the hallway, up the stair well and all over one of the public bathrooms before he got back to the room.

We had an "interesting" seven days.

I'm not sure how much weight my son lost.

He was fine whenever we were at a port for eight hours but was always "green" whenever we were at sea.

In one of my weaker moments I'm sure I said something along the lines of "come on, just snap out of it."

I only said it once.

My wife's glare was enough to snap me back into acting more appropriately.

I've never been sea sick.

I've never even had a bad case of vertigo.

I'm sure I would have some pretty choice words if someone told me to just snap out of it.

Needless to say, we won't be going on another family cruise for awhile.

Whenever I even start to think about bringing up the topic for discussion I remember our last trip.

No one has to tell me to "snap out of it."

FORTY-THREE: DON'T TELL MY KIDS

My kids have been doing really well in school so far.

My son is finishing 8th grade and my daughter 7th grade.

Both have had straight A's for the most part.

Both ace all the standard tests they are required to take.

Both have received many awards from school.

All my wife and I have ever said is that we would always like them to do their best.

I was never a very good student at their age.

All I really cared about were sports.

Don't tell them...OK?

As the youngest of four kids, I had a lot more slack from my parents then my brothers and sister had through school.

Either that or they were just plum tired of closely tracking our grades.

I never actually remember being told I needed to do better in school.

I think I also received sort of a "pass" at times, from many teachers, since my older siblings had all been good students.

I even got a D one semester, in 9th grade, in Foreign Language.

I'm know at least once I forged a parent signature on a report card.

I'm sure it was the semester I received the D.

In general, I was pretty much a "C" student until the end of 9th grade.

That spring we went on a trip to visit my older brothers who were in college.

My sister was also interested in going to the same school and she got a bunch of information from the admissions office.

It was a really nice school.

There seemed to be some great athletic facilities and although I wouldn't admit it at the time, there were also a lot of good looking girls walking around the campus as well.

I was bored on the car trip home since it was an approximate six hour trip from New York.

I started looking through the admissions material.

It had the grade point averages listed for the most recent classes admitted.

Holy smoke, I thought to myself.

I guess I better start doing better in school!

The academic "light bulb" went on for the first time in my life.

I started to take school work seriously and did really well for the last three years of high school.

I was elected into our school's National Honor Society.

I even got a partial academic scholarship for college.

My two brothers, sister and I all went to the University of Virginia.

We were all there during my first year; my oldest brother in graduate school, my sister third year and my other brother fourth year.

I think my kids sort of assume I was always a good student since I'm a doctor.

Now you know the truth (as will they when they are old enough to read this book).

I've never told them about my checkered academic past from when I was a kid.

I figure I'll just wait until one of them gets a bad grade, for the first time, and then I'll confess.

In the mean time it will be "our" secret.

FORTY-FOUR: DO AS I SAY, NOT AS I DID

On reflection, I was clearly depressed when I went through a mid-life crisis a few years ago.

I questioned my desire to remain a physician. I investigated becoming a teacher and obtained a three year temporary teaching certificate from the Florida Department of Education. I gave three months notice for leaving my practice. I interviewed for some teaching positions. At the same time, I felt like Huck Finn going to his own wake, as many patients said some of the most heart warming things possible to me (many said by those I would have previously deemed to be my "problem" patients).

I lost my self confidence. I had an altered sense of body image. I lost my appetite. I became reclusive. I had various bodily aches and pains. I had a hard time concentrating. I was anxious and irritable. I started to read the Bible daily. I stopped exercising. I had severe insomnia.

I'll admit that I never knew how terrible insomnia could be.

The worst time of my day was about 9:00 PM. That was usually the time my wife and kids would go to bed. I was then alone, except for the multiple times I would arouse my wife to "talk for awhile."

She was amazing. She revealed her true character and commitment to our marriage. Although I'm sure she was probably freaking out, she remained supportive and caring.

I would usually stay out in the living room until I couldn't keep my eyes open any longer. Then I would sneak back to the bedroom.

Once in bed with my eyes closed, the slide show would start. I would see what looked like an old slide projector flashing images in front of me. Images that had to do, it seemed, with my previous 45 years on earth. Every aspect of my life would appear, in no particular order: old friends, old enemies, previous decisions, career choices, financial issues, etc.

I couldn't sleep on my stomach. My heart was pounding so hard I would feel like I was bouncing on the bed.

The slide show would stop whenever I would open my eyes. I would try to keep them open for as long a possible.

It's amazing how long a night can be when only asleep for about an hour and a half.

I discovered the 24 hour Wal-Mart and Denny's near our home.

I tried everything over the counter I could think of such as herbal tea, warm milk, melatonin, antihistamines and even small amounts of alcohol. Nothing seemed to help.

Suicide was an occasional fleeting thought.

I finally called my sister Eva and had some great conversations.

She also just happens to be a psychiatrist.

She was amazingly helpful.

I was finally convinced to call my personal physician.

I set up an appointment.

My wife came with me.

My family doctor felt I was depressed.

He went to his medication closet and brought back some samples.

He also recommended that I set up an appointment with a counselor.

When he left the exam room I immediately gave the samples to my wife to hide them in her pocket book. I didn't want anyone to see me walking out with samples for a commonly known antidepressant.

I wasn't depressed, I told myself. All I needed was to get a good night sleep.

He had also given me samples of a commonly advertised sleeping pill. The same pill that states to not take unless you have the ability to get eight hours of uninterrupted sleep.

I took the first one that night at 11 PM, prepared to wake up a new man at approximately 7 AM.

I woke up at about 12:15 AM. I had only been asleep for a little over an hour!

I took two the next night and slept for about an hour and a half.

I called my physician again.

He said the antidepressants would take a couple of weeks to start working.

I knew that.

I had told my patients the same thing over the years.

I just didn't tell him I hadn't started to take them yet.

I spent a lot of time staring at the package but I couldn't seem to actually allow myself to swallow one.

He called in a stronger sleeping pill.

I took the first one that night. I slept for about four hours.

After about four to five days of getting some sleep I started to feel a lot better.

I could think clearer.

I even started the antidepressant tablets.

I decided to remain a doctor who teaches, instead of being a teacher who used to be a doctor.

For me it was incredibly comforting to remember what I wanted to do "when I grow up."

The depression lifted relatively quickly.

I stopped the antidepressant tablets after about two months.

I tapered and stopped the sleeping pills over the same amount of time.

It's still hard for me to accept the fact I was a nut case for about four months.

I hesitated to seek treatment for over two months.

While not trying to sound too dramatic, it felt like the longest two months of my life.

It has given me a lot more empathy for my patients.

It's definitely given me a sense of urgency in trying to help those with concerns of depression, anxiety, and insomnia, as well as the inevitable thoughts of suicide.

I've told patients my personal story at times, especially to those who didn't want to ask for help or were hesitant to try medications. I tell them to do as I say, not as I did. They owe it to themselves and their family to seek treatment as early as possible.

FORTY-FIVE: STAYING ON THE MENTAL HEALTH FRONTIER

1. I've never been a huge fan of public speaking. Probably my worst bout of performance anxiety occurred while in court over twenty years ago.

My first rotation while a medical intern was in the Emergency Room. I performed a PERK (physical evidence rape kit) exam on a woman and was later subpoenaed to appear in court to review my exam and findings at the time.

The district attorney told me it would be no big deal.

When I got called in to testify the court room was packed.

Immediately my heart started to pound and the waterfalls in my arm pits started.

The first question seemed to be the hardest, "please state your name."

My voice was quivering to such a great degree I suspect it was hard to hear what I said.

My voice settled down a little after that but it still left a lasting impression on me.

I still haven't resorted to any medications yet for public speaking.

I usually just re-tell the above story about my court appearance.

Acknowledging to the audience my past episode of extreme performance anxiety tends to help me relax and regain control of my voice.

2. I'm sure a lot of physicians have obsessive compulsive traits. I know I do. I suspect that many are too embarrassed to reveal theirs.

I remember visiting with a physician years ago at his house. He had just finished raking the leaves in his front yard when I arrived. While we were talking, ONE leaf fell from a tree on to the middle of the yard. While talking he felt the need to walk over and pick it up. I suspect this was one of his OCD habits.

I enjoyed the movie a few years ago with Nicholas Cage called "Matchstick Men."

In the movie he plays a con artist with OCD. He had such traits as needing to have all the carpet lines from the vacuum aligned perfectly before leaving a room.

Come on, what are your OCD traits?

Here are mine (and I'm sure my wife and kids would confirm the same):

1. Emptying all the trash cans in the house and having the couch pillows "in alignment" before leaving town to go away for the day or on vacation.

2. Having clean floor mats in my car.

So far my OCD traits have remained manageable. I've given my wife permission, however, to call in the experts if I start turning the lights on and off three times before entering or leaving a room.

3. (I know...at this point you're really starting to question my sanity) Nervous tics; they seem to run in my family.

I had nervous tics when I was young.

I used to have the need to adjust my genitals when I was a kid. I distinctly remember I didn't have a rash or an itch; I just needed to frequently perform an "adjustment." It drove my mother crazy. I couldn't really explain to her why I NEEDED to do it. I'm pretty sure I remember being taken to our doctor more than once to see if I had a problem.

The best part of playing little league baseball was I could place my glove "down there" and use my other hand to secretly do a quick adjustment. However, every time I would look up my mother would be glaring at me to stop.

Yes, I'm happy to say I did grow out of it.

My only remaining tic is a sort of neck writhing movement I do when wearing a dress shirt with a tie. I don't really know why. It just feels good to do it.

My wife also had a nervous tic. She used to do some sort of an exaggerated yawning movement when she was young. It also used to annoy her mother. She also reports it just felt good to do it. She also outgrew her tic.

Whenever my daughter was stressed she made a twitching movement of her nose and a soft clucking sound with her tongue on the roof of her mouth.

My son had the most noticeable nervous tics. The most consistent was his desire to smell his fingers. Having been a "tic-er" I recognized his attempts to incorporate it into his other movements. He would brush his hair to the side and then grab a quick smell of his fingers on the way down. He would pretend to scratch his nose and take a quick smell.

Again, the frequency was always more pronounced when stressed with school or sports.

One night over dinner my wife and I decided to broach the topic with our kids. I started first. Everyone was cracking up by the time I was finished coming clean about my past history of nervous tics. My wife went next. More laughter followed, especially when she had such vivid memories of her mother's desire to get her to stop.

Next, my kids started to talk about their own tics. They obviously were aware they had them. I think they were surprised to know we had noticed. They acknowledged they worsened with stress but were able to laugh and poke fun at themselves in a safe setting.

Almost immediately the tics improved. Both kids had a significant decrease in the frequency of their tics.

Laughter, again, was the best medicine.

Either that or they were just relieved to find out my wife and I also had nervous tics and had "grown out" of them over the years.

FORTY-SIX: MORE STORIES FROM THE PERSPECTIVE OF BEING A PATIENT

1. "I thought the coupon was for a pair of glasses for $99," said my wife while looking at a checkbook entry for almost $300.

"It was", I answered, "but that didn't include the polycarbonate lenses, scratch resistance, ultraviolet light filter or the flexible hinges on the arms. Those were all extra."

2. "Why did you put your clothes back on?" remarked the nurse at the dermatologist office, when she finally walked in with the dermatologist for my skin exam.

"Because I've been sitting in this room for about 45 minutes with my clothes off and got tired of staring at my love handles in the mirror," I responded.

3. "I can't seem to focus with my new glasses," I mentioned to my wife for about two weeks.

"Give it time, it just takes a little while to adjust," my wife would respond.

"It takes a little time to adjust to a new prescription," said the eye technician when I called the optometry office.

After two weeks I finally went back to the optometrist.

"You have the wrong prescription in your left lens," said the eye technician, after checking my lenses against the prescription.

"Where did you have the glasses made?"

"Here", I replied, "you fit them on me when I picked them up."

"Oh", she said defensively.

"I'm not mad, I just glad I'm not losing my mind. I felt drunk every time I've tried to wear them for the last two weeks."

"Why didn't you alternate opening and closing an eye to look through the lenses?" said my matter of fact wife on returning home with my new-new pair of glasses.

"I've never been able to voluntarily shut just my right eye. I didn't think about holding it shut with my hand," was the only thing I could add.

4. "Did you take any kind of sedation prior to coming in?" asked the radiology MRI technician. I had been sent to have an MRI of my hip by an orthopedic surgeon.

"No", I replied, "I'm pretty sure I won't need any."

"OK, then, let's start."

The technician then pushed me inside the coffin, I mean the MRI machine. There was a puff of air going across my face and some soft music playing. When I opened my eyes I had only a few inches of space available between my head and the inside of the tube. I kept my eyes closed.

Shortly after, what sounded like about 10,000 jack hammers began. It was the sound generated by the magnetic fields being established. I could no longer hear the soft music.

I talked to myself and tried to relax.

My only thought was, "My God, you've got to be kidding me!" I had no idea.

I was claustrophobic and I've never been claustrophobic.

After about 15 minutes I was pulled out of the machine.

"How many folks lose it while in this MRI machine (a closed MRI)?"

"About 50%," replied the tech.

"Wow," I said, but honestly I was surprised the percentage wasn't closer to 100%.

I've let patients know about my experience prior to sending them for a closed MRI exam and offer sedation whenever they mention they might not be comfortable lying in a coffin with the lid shut.

5. "Why don't you get your heel checked out; I'm tired of hearing you complain about it!" said my wife.

I had been having left heel pain for about a year.

Jerry Seinfeld used to joke we take our feet for granted. We only think about them when they hurt. Otherwise the only thing we ever do for them is let water drip down on top of them whenever we take a shower.

My heel was killing me. Especially when getting up to urinate in the middle of the night.

I was sure it was plantar fasciitis. It just hadn't responded to any of the conservative measures I had offered my patients over the years.

After having the pain for so long I just wanted to make sure I didn't have a fracture or anything else going on.

I set up an appointment.

The orthopedic foot specialist was quite a bit younger than me.

After listening to my history I'm sure I saw him roll his eyes. I took it to mean "You're a doctor, why are you wasting my time with such a trivial concern."

He "allowed" me to get an x-ray.

It was completely normal.

He reviewed the same conservative treatment measures I had been employing for the last year.

He offered to do a steroid injection.

I declined.

That weekend I went to a shoe store with my wife.

I've always had a habit of walking around a shoe store and zeroing in on the least expensive shoes and sneakers that I could find in the store and buying them; no matter the quality.

She "made" me purchase two good pair of dress shoes as well as a pair of the most expensive sneakers I had ever bought (over $70!).

I wore the sneakers home.

I felt the pain almost instantly start to disappear with every step I took in my new gel filled wonders.

Within 3 days, I was pain free.

I've had no pain since.

I now have changed my initial recommendations for those dealing with plantar fasciitis.

Don't be a cheapskate when it comes to shoe wear.

FORTY-SEVEN: YOUNGER THAN I LOOK

I've been prematurely grey for a number of years.

My kids usually don't even give me credit for the color grey.

They say my hair is white.

I still feel young and actually think I look pretty young. About the only time I really feel old is when I look at a photograph. Even looking into a mirror does not give me the same reality check as does a photograph for some reason.

I recently went to my 30th high school reunion.

Someone would approach and comment I looked nothing like I used to look. The next person would come up and say I hadn't changed a bit.

Obviously, I was able to deduce the truth was actually somewhere between the two extremes.

I've had many patients over the years assume I was older than I am.

To be honest, I've had my feelings hurt a few times. Especially when I'm looking at a person who looks VERY old and he/she makes a comment along the lines of "You know how it is for people our age."

Occasionally it pays to have your feelings hurt, however.

I recently went to pick up my car after some engine work was performed.

The cashier at the auto shop pulled my work sheet and without looking at me said it would be $380 for the work done.

After he looked up at me, however, he added, "Oh, but that's before your 10% senior citizen discount." I was 46 y/o at the time.

The final cost was $342.

When I got home my wife and kids shared in a good laugh.

"What did you say?" asked my wife.

"I said Thanks. I figured if he was going to insult me I would take the discount and hope he put me down in their data base for the same discount in the future."

FORTY-EIGHT: WHAT?

I hate to admit it…

I'm going to need hearing aids in the future. I'm just not ready to wear (accept) them yet.

I'm sure my wife wanted me to have them YESTERDAY.

I keep telling her I do have a hard time hearing what she is saying, while in the kitchen with the dishwasher and washing machine on, and, while she is walking away from me.

She also says I keep the TV too loud.

She's got a point there.

My kids second that thought.

All three of them often go the bed, after we've watched a movie together, complaining their ears are ringing because the volume was so loud.

I also can't always explain why I hear some of the things I think I hear. I always know I did something really stupid when my wife and kids are laughing at me.

"Yes, I'd like a really, really large glass of water," I announce to the waitress who just asked us a question.

"Why are all you guys laughing at me?" I ask my wife and kids after the waitress has left to get my water.

"The waitress just asked if anyone tonight was celebrating a special occasion" said my wife.

"Oh, that's weird; I could have sworn she asked what I wanted to drink."

Or even another weirder episode.

"I also heard the movie Little Miss Sunshine is excellent," I announce in response to a question at home while eating dinner.

"Why are you guys laughing at me again?"

"Because I just asked if any basketball games were on TV tonight," said my son.

"Oh."

I'll just start to say "what" in response to most questions.

I don't want them to worry yet that I'm also getting demented.

I prefer to just be losing my hearing at this stage of my life.

FORTY-NINE: A $715 LIFE-SAVER

I've had many patients addicted to substances over the years.

The most common addictions, of course, have been to nicotine and alcohol.

Others have been addicted to cocaine and heroin.

I'm also a recovered addict.

There weren't any support groups for my problem.

If there were I would need to say: "Hi, my name is Bill, I'm a recovered Wint-O-Green life saver addict."

I went cold turkey on my own.

I wasn't able to locate any Wint-O-Green life saver anonymous meetings.

A $715 life saver also helped motivate me to quit.

I used to buy a big bag of Wint-O-Green life savers almost every day I was in the office seeing patients. Not a roll of life savers, a bag.

I would try to put out only a limited number everyday but would invariably go through those, as well as the rest of the bag...especially during a stressful day.

I gained some weight...obviously. They're approximately 15 calories a pop.

I would tell myself I was going to suck each to completion but would pretty much always bite down before allowing this to happen.

I'm not sure of the ingredient that made them so habit forming.

I think this information is kept in a top secret file by the candy company.

One day I bit down and thought there was a rock in the life saver.

Initially, I figured I might be able to call one of the attorneys I see on TV every night to sue the candy company.

Then I felt my cracked tooth.

The partial crown to cover the defect cost $715.

I've been Wint-O-Green free for about 5 years now.

I have come across others with the same addiction.

I periodically look at the dentist bill.

That, and turning my head away when passing a candy stand, is all the therapy I've needed to remain clean.

FIFTY: MY WIFE'S ADDICTION

My wife has had a fairly squeaky clean past; as best I can tell.

I know she had some pretty "wild" older step sisters, however.

I think they might have helped to orchestrate any past history of indiscretions when she was younger.

There's never been any reason to re-hash our past exploits.

I met my wife when she was 18.

We met in a medical library.

She was in nursing school.

I was 27.

You can imagine the grief I got from my friends.

We didn't start dating, however, until she was 20.

We got married when she was 23 (I was 32).

We've never smoked cigarettes.

Neither of us drinks alcohol except on a very rare occasion.

The only "chemicals" ingested have always been prescribed.

She does have an addiction however.

It's Diet Coke.

She NEEDS to have at least two cans a day.

If she doesn't have her daily fix she can be quite unpleasant.

This is a fact.

She knows it.

Our kids know it.

We have shelves in the back of our garage.

We almost always have at least a case of Diet Coke on stand-by.

We occasionally run out of milk, or some other staple, but we always have Diet Coke.

I think the lowest amount we have ever had was a twelve pack in reserve.

May be we should combine our addictions.

We could put some Wint-O-Green life savers in a can of Diet Coke and see what happens.

Aren't we a wild and crazy couple?

I bet you all want to party with us, don't you?

FIFTY-ONE: DON'T TALK TO ANYONE IN THE WAITING ROOM

Deciding to have an elective surgery is never an easy decision.

Many operations are elective. Some of the more common examples are joint replacement and back surgery.

I had a hip replacement about eleven years ago, when I was in my late 30's, due to hip dysplasia, pain and locking. My quality of life at the time pretty much stunk.

My wife was instrumental in getting me to recognize my disability. In retrospect, it was a great decision. I've been active and pain free since. However, the decision to proceed with surgery wasn't necessarily an easy one to make.

Although I've had many patients do very well after joint replacement surgery, I could only remember a few specific patients in the days leading up to my planned surgery date.

They included all the patients I knew who had done poorly or had a post operative complication.

I lost a lot of sleep thinking about those patients. Luckily, my support system was strong.

Many folks don't have a strong support system.

I always tell people who are considering joint replacement surgery, or any elective operation, to NOT talk to anyone in the waiting room of a doctor's office.

Unless they are there for a routine visit, many of the folks in the waiting room represent the small number of people who had an elective surgery and are no better or, in some cases, are even worse.

It's obviously hard to proceed with an elective surgery if you meet a few patients in a waiting room who had the same surgery you're contemplating and had complications.

All elective surgeries have a risk.

Even if the risk of a procedure is only 3-5%, it's 100% for those who have the complication or adverse outcome.

Instead, talk to folks you meet while out shopping, golfing, fishing etc.

You'll be surprised how many have had an elective procedure done and it will definitely put you in a better frame of mind when getting ready to have the procedure done on yourself.

FIFTY-TWO: HE CAN'T PUT MY NAME ANYWHERE

A 53 y/o male moved here from another state. It was our first visit together. He was with a woman.

Me: Hi, welcome. How are you related?

Patient: She's my fiancée.

Me: Congratulations. What brought you to Florida from Maryland?

Patient: I needed to get away from my wife.

Me: Oh. Are you still married?

Patient: Yes, but she didn't have my best interests at heart, so I went back with my girlfriend.

Me: You mean fiancée?

Patient: Yes.

I decided not to go into the whole "you can't have a fiancée while your still married issue." A little while later during the physical exam I noticed he had a bunch of tattoos.

Me: Who's Kay (he had Kay tattooed on the left deltoid region and on the back of his left hand)?

Patient: My second wife.

Me: Who's Brenda (name tattooed on left forearm surrounded by a heart)?

Patient: My first wife.

Me: Who's Chelsea (tattooed on the back of the right hand)?

Patient: My third wife.

Me: Who's Sue (tattooed on the right forearm)?

Patient: My current wife.

Finally his "fiancée" speaks up. "I'm Kathy; I've already told him he can't put my name anywhere!"

FIFTY-THREE: NOT A GOOD TIME TO QUIT

Mr. B was a 46 y/o male with high blood pressure and diabetes. He also smoked two packs a day of cigarettes. We had the following encounter:

Me: Have you given any thought toward trying to quit smoking?

Mr. B: Yeah, but it's not a good time right now.

Me: Really, what's up?

Mr. B: You really want to know?

Me: Sure (although I suspect I might not have sounded too convincing).

Mr. B: Let's see...a year ago I was living alone in my three bedrooms, one bath mobile home. I got re-married about ten months ago...about three months after that her brother moved in with us because he lost his job and had no place to live...a few weeks after that her daughter moved in with her dead-beat boyfriend, three children, two cats and a dog. Last week I drove up to West Virginia to help my son, his wife and their four kids move here because he lost his job and was going to be evicted from their apartment. I have fourteen people living at my house right now and the animals. All the bedrooms are taken up and my son and his family are camped out in the rest of the house. I'm also the only one working. My only enjoyment is smoking so I'm not going to try to quit right now.

When he saw me starting to grin he started to laugh a little as well.

I let him know I wasn't laughing at him, just his excellent skills at painting a picture of his life at this time.

He let me know this was the first time he had actually completely verbalized his situation and he agreed it was so sad it was funny.

We spent some time trying to problem solve a little and I think he left feeling a little better.

I also let him know that we were in agreement.

It was not a good time to try to quit smoking.

FIFTY-FOUR: A MATTER OF PRINCIPLE

A 47 y/o male was in the midst of some hard times. He had been diagnosed with heart disease at an early age and recently had a prolonged hospitalization. He was also financially strapped.

Me: How are things going?

Patient: Pretty rough. My hours were cut back from 40 to 28 but all my other expenses have remained the same. I've got rent to pay on my apartment and my child support payments are deducted from my check each week.

Me: How many kids do you have?

Patient: Two, they both live with their mother. One daughter is 11 and the other is 14.

Me: How long have you been separated from your children?

Patient: Ever since their mother left with them. When I had my first heart attack she left while I was still in the hospital. She still lives nearby but doesn't let me visit my children very often.

Me: How long have you been apart?

Patient: About 9 years. We're still married but she's been with a different guy for the last 8 years. She has two more children with him.

Me: Why haven't you gotten a divorce?

Patient: It's a matter of principle. I told her when we got married that nobody in my family has ever gotten divorced. It's a family tradition. I told her that if we ever got divorced she would have to do it. I want a divorce but I'm not going to apply for one or pay for one. It costs about $300 and I'm not going to go against my principles.

Me: What if you meet someone else?

Patient: I already have. We want to get married but can't because I'm still married. I know it sounds strange but I think I'll win this disagreement as long as I don't back down now after all these years.

Me: OK, good luck with that. I'll look forward to getting an update the next time you come in for an appointment. Do you have any other long standing matter of principle family traditions?

He laughed.

FIFTY-FIVE: HELL NO

A 68 y/o male came in for his first visit.

Me: Tell me about yourself.

Patient: I've been laying tile for about 40 years now but I'm also a pastor.

Me: A pastor?

Patient: Yes, a Baptist preacher. It's my life calling, my passion. It fills me with a sense of purpose. It gives me hope for the future. I still preach at a small church two days a week.

Me: That's great; awesome…I bet you're planning on preaching for the rest of your life.

Patient: Hell no…I plan to retire as soon as I pay off my Ford Crown Victoria…it's a 2004…I got a good deal on it, but the church only has about 50 members and the donation I get for preaching there every week isn't much.

Me (I suspect after my usual stunned stare): Cool, good luck with that; sounds exciting.

I didn't think it would be appropriate to help with some simple math (even though I had a calculator handy):

(Money due on Ford Crown Victoria) divided by (Average portion of weekly church donation put toward the car) = the end of a life calling

FIFTY-SIX: NEEDING TO SEE A BONE SPECIALIST

A 74 y/o male was in for a routine f/u appt.

He had retired to the south, from the northeast, a few years ago.

I knew he loved sports.

In the midst of briefly socializing I let him know I had recently been up north to attend a high school reunion. I went to a local pub with some friends and I was pretty sure the bartender was probably a sports "bookie." I went on to describe what I had seen. The bartenders name was even "Pauli," just like in the movies.

 He agreed my assumption was probably correct.

He then continued.

"When I was younger I owned a bar and took numbers."

"You did?"

He went on to explain.

"I ran a good business...running the numbers just helped to increase the profits."

"Didn't you run the risk of getting caught or folks not wanting to pay off their debts?"

"The cops were some of my best customers. I never had a problem with them because they knew I ran an honest business. Everyday I would tape all the incoming phone calls in case someone tried to postdate a bet or in case they didn't want to pay. I would play the tape back to them with the day and time of the call. I would let them hear their voice and then just say try to screw me again and you'll need to see a bone specialist. They got the point real quick."

We both laughed.

That night I shared the story with my wife.

There's just something so "Soprano-like" about the term "bone specialist" (especially when said by someone with a northeast, actually a New York, accent). I'm sure it helped the customers think about all their bones. The term "orthopedic surgeon" would never have conjured up the same images in a person's mind!

FIFTY-SEVEN: MORE PATIENT ENCOUNTERS

* A male who has hypertension, diabetes and erectile dysfunction came in for a follow-up appointment. He failed to have improved sexual functioning with the use of an external vacuum pump, oral medications or injections. He finally had a penile implant placed.

Patient: Everything is going well except the head doesn't get hard.

Me: I'm sorry, what?

Patient: The shaft gets hard when I inflate the implant but the head doesn't get hard. I'm not in a relationship yet, so I haven't actually done a field test yet, but I want to make sure I have all the tools of the trade when the opportunity arises.

I had to break the sad news that a "penile head hardening tool" wasn't available just yet. He was a retired engineer, in case you couldn't have guessed!

* A 53 y/o women came in for an acute visit.

Patient: I took my blood sugar last night and the glucometer just said "high." I said "Hi, how are you," back to it and called this morning for an appointment.

Her blood sugar reading at the lab was 520!

* Patient: My other doctor gave me a peace pipe…you know a smoke pipe sort of thing…do you think I need one again?

After concluding that he wasn't a native Indian and that his previous doctor wasn't a witch doctor, we eventually came to the conclusion he had previously used a nebulizer machine for breathing treatments.

* Patient: The orthopedic doctor gave me a shot of chromosome (cortisone) in my knee but it didn't help.

* Patient: The stomach doctor said I have a hellava (hiatal) hernia.

I hadn't seen the results of the upper endoscopy yet but maybe he did have a "hellava hiatal hernia."

* Patient: I'm pretty sure I have a high-tail (hiatal) hernia. My brother had one and had the same symptoms I've got.

*Me (on seeing a 76 y/o male with an upper respiratory infection. His wife was with him): Has anyone else at home been sick?

(I was trying to see if any other family members had upper respiratory tract symptoms)

Wife: Our son and daughter-in-law have been real sick.

Me: Do they live with you?

Wife: Yes.

Me: What symptoms have they had?

Wife: My son's back has been killing him. He was helping to rearrange some furniture and thinks he might have thrown out his back. He also has glaucoma and he's been out of work since his prostate surgery. My daughter-in-law has been having heavy menstrual bleeding and is having some tests to see if she is going through the change of life. Her doctor thinks it the menstrual-pause (menopause). She has diabetes and hasn't been following her diet since my son's been sick.

Me: Oh, I see...thanks.

I know...I should have asked the question better in the first place. I just felt fortunate she only updated me on two other family members (who weren't my patients) unrelated medical problems.

*Me: Do you smoke?

Patient: No cigarettes, just an occasional doobie.

Me: A doobie?

Patient: Yeah, you know, grass, some pot.

Me: Yeah, I do know. It's just a term I hadn't heard used for close to thirty years.

FIFTY-EIGHT: SOME DOOBIE MEMORIES

I went to high school in the 1970's.

I was a "smart jock" and some considered me a "big fish on campus" my senior year.

I considered myself well informed and in touch with my friends.

Over the years I've come to realize I may have been a big-fish, but in a very small puddle and determined I wasn't always well informed or in touch.

It wasn't until after I graduated that I found out some friends had been drinking alcohol and smoking pot while in high school.

The first time I ever drank alcohol was during the summer between high school and college. It was a reality check to find myself drunk and hearing some of my friends laughing at me because they saw me kissing a girl I barely knew while lying in some bushes. I never smoked pot.

I started college in 1977 at the University of Virginia. I lived with nine other guys in a dormitory suite. We had a central living room that was surrounded by five bedrooms and a bath.

My 1st year college roommate was a great guy. He was a good old southern boy. He drank beer almost every day. He smoked pot almost every day. He used his desk for two things. On one half he had a fish tank. On the other half he had pot plants growing in little cups under a special UV light. Many of the other guys in the suite smoked pot frequently, some almost every day as well.

Every other suite had a resident advisor (RA). We didn't have one. We had very little supervision. Occasionally our RA would poke his head into our suite. I would often be sitting in the living room area alone, as the other nine guys were in somebody's room smoking pot. He would ask how everything was going and I'd say "fine" and he'd leave.

A lot of the time the suite mates sat in a room passing around a little moist remnant of a joint that was precariously perched on top of a roach clip.

Some of the guys had bongs. I had also never seen one of these prior to going to college. The old bong water would stink. One day I also saw one of the suite mates scrapping what looked like mud on to a peanut butter sandwich. He let me know it was hashish after I turned down his offer to try some.

I was never pressured to start smoking pot. My roommate would occasionally offer me some knowing I would decline. It actually became sort of a joke between us for the year.

He never smoked in our room.

One day during our first year we had a knock on our bedroom door. It was his Aunt and Uncle. They had come to let him know his father had died the night before. That afternoon, prior to his leaving for the funeral, I accepted his invitation to take a drag of a joint. I felt it was sort of a roommate bonding moment. I can't really say I felt anything. I haven't smoked pot since.

Although I suspect my mother will be quite shocked to read this, I also want her to know I didn't really inhale, just like former President Clinton!

Of the ten of us who shared the suite together during our first year in college:

One (the guy with the peanut butter hashish sandwich) dropped out of school. No one really knows what happened to him.

One is a national sales rep for a major framing company (my roommate).

Two are doctors (including me).

One is a commercial pilot.

One is an accountant.

One is an attorney.

One is a home builder.

The remaining two are both employed and productive members of society. I lost contact with them and don't know exactly what they are doing career-wise.

I would assume that a lot of folks who went to college in the 1970's have their own doobie memories.

Am I correct?

FIFTY-NINE: DO I HAVE ENOUGH FRIENDS?

I'm approaching 50 years of age.

Both of my brothers had big "surprise" birthday parties when they turned 50.

A bunch of family and "friends" came to their parties.

"Are you going to throw me a surprise 50th birthday party?" I asked my wife.

"Sure," she said, "I'll invite all your friends."

I know she was implying it would be a very small party.

That got me thinking.

Do I need more friends?

I have a lot of acquaintances, but very few friends.

Maybe my definition of a "friend" is more stringent than most?

My definition: a friend is someone who has made a unique and long lasting impact on your life and whose life you will contemplate and honor by your thoughts if/when they die.

Everyone else, besides family, is an acquaintance.

Here's a typical conversation overheard at work sometimes:

"Did you hear that _____ (fill in the name) died?"

"You're kidding; he/she was such a good friend. Wow, that's too bad...hey where do you want to go to lunch today?"

There are a number of guys I've known over the years who meet my definition of a friend.

Some I haven't seen for years.

I don't have a lot of gal friends (other than my wife). I really only had a few long term relationships prior to meeting my wife.

I would consider all of them to still be friends.

I can't say I've actively pursued making a lot of new friends over the last number of years, especially since I've been a husband and a father.

I love my wife.

She understands me.

She knows I spend such a huge part of my day talking (as does she in her profession) and sometimes I'm just plum tired of talking.

My wife knows my silence, usually, does not mean anything other than I'm just enjoying being quiet.

It's usually necessary to talk to cultivate a possible new friend.

I also love my kids.

I love being involved in every aspect of their lives; within reason of course.

Having too many friends, at this stage of my life, might take away from "family time."

Many of the nice people I meet (who could possibly become a new friend) seem to have the same family priorities.

So if my wife throws me a "surprise" party (I'll pretend to be surprised!) and only invites family and friends, it will be a small party.

If she invites all my acquaintances it will look more impressive, but it still won't have as many as my brother's parties.

But I'm fine with that.

I think I have enough friends for now.

I've got plenty of time to make some more friends.

After all, I'm only half-way to 100!

SIXTY: SAME THING, DIFFERENT YEAR

This year was going to be different. We sent out a newsletter to all our patients to explain, in simplistic terms, upper respiratory infections, viral syndromes, and the flu. The symptoms were described, as was the potential 5-7 day duration. Preventative measures were detailed, and all available symptomatic therapies were discussed. Treatment recommendations were broad and simple. They included the importance of drinking 6-8 glasses of water a day, the use of analgesics, expectorants, short term use of nasal decongestants, possible use of Vitamin C, throat lozenges, zinc, herbal supplements, cough suppressants, steam, chicken noodle soup, increased rest, etc. We encouraged people to get the flu shot. We discussed some of the new treatments available for influenza. A lengthy discussion then followed about the fact that antibiotics didn't play a role in the treatment of most cases, as did a discussion on the dangers of antibiotic resistance for both individuals and society as a whole.

Other years I have, at times, dreaded going to my office during the cold and flu season. I enjoy most of my patients. I just get tired of having to repeat the same canned talk over and over again.

I have also written more than my share of antibiotics for colds. I always spend time reviewing patient's symptoms and do an examination. I explain their diagnosis and symptomatic treatment measures, as well as often discuss why they don't need antibiotics. I even review my approach to treating my family members. They thank me for the explanation and then often say, "But aren't you still going to give me antibiotics?"

163

Even many who seemed convinced they didn't need antibiotics would often call back a few days later. They wanted me to know that they had gone to an urgent care center and that the doctor there had spent only a couple of minutes with them to know they needed "that pack thing, you know, the five day thing, the six pills, Z pack, yeah a Z pack."

We've been back in the cold season for a number of weeks now. Most folks who come in with symptoms state they didn't use any symptomatic medications because they didn't want to mask their symptoms or they wanted me to see just how bad they were feeling.

Most say they read the newsletter we mailed to them. They appreciated the information.

However, they would appreciate a prescription for antibiotics even more. They have a friend or co-worker who had the same symptoms. Luckily they went to their doctor right away and got the "five day thing, the six pills, you know the Z pack thing."

Oh well, maybe next year will be different.

SIXTY-ONE: TAPE RECORDED COMMENTS

All physicians come up with certain comments in response to questions. Sometimes I feel like a tape recorder, hearing myself say the same thing repeatedly. At least, as a family doctor, I get a lot of variety to the questions asked, unlike some specialists.

During my residency I did a one-month rotation with an allergist. He was a machine. He was incredibly efficient, saw a ton of patients but said the same thing over and over and over again to most of his new patients.

Over twenty years removed I can still hear a couple of his comments made to all patients:

1. "A lot of my other patients want to know if you can outgrow allergies. If that were the case I would love to tell them to just please grow up."
2. "I don't want to be an albatross around your neck but I also won't put you on a freight train and wave good-bye. If you decide to start allergy shots, you must always, you must always, you must always (always repeated three times) get your first shots of any new vial here in my office."

My thoughts at the time were I had picked the correct branch of medicine. To know a little about a lot was more sanity promoting, for me, than knowing a lot about a little.

Nonetheless, I still have a couple of comments that have stood the test of time. Some have been used to ease an obvious tension in a room with a patient and their family. Others, perhaps, have been used to bring in some laughter.

Here are some of my more frequently used comments:

* When seeing a patient that has been waiting for a long time:

#1 "I'm sorry you've had such a long wait. I know your time is important, and again, I'm sorry you've had a long wait."

#2 "I'm sorry to keep you waiting so long. My brother always calls the exam room a holding chamber. You get put in the room, hear people walking back and forth outside but never quite know when the door might open for your turn."

* When seeing a patient who has been waiting a LONG time due to coming to the clinic without an appointment:

"I'm sorry you've had such a long wait and don't feel well, but I'm glad you're here and I hope I can help."

* When answering a question such as will I need to take this medication for the rest of my life? (When initiating a medication for a chronic illness):

"It's possible if all medical research stops today. I'll try to stay abreast of any new changes or treatments for your condition and would expect for you to do the same. Let me know if you come across anything in your research as well."

Along the same lines, occasionally I need to initiate insulin therapy for elderly patients. A number of years ago, an 81 y/o male got visibly upset and teary eyed when I recommended we begin insulin therapy. He asked the same question, "Will I need to take the insulin for the rest of my life?"

I said I thought he would only need to take it for the next ten years. He responded he didn't think he would be alive in ten years.

After a thoughtful pause he started to laugh, as did I. I have used the same response, for a situation such as this, since, with equally good results.

* I used to perform flexible sigmoidoscopies once a week for colorectal cancer screening. In discussing the risks of the procedure I would let them know it's estimated one in five hundred procedures could have a complication. I would then often add:

"But I've done four hundred and ninety-nine so far and never had a problem." Most would get the joke and start to laugh.

* When trying to discuss a medication that is not available on a drug formulary:

"It's an excellent medication. I'm very familiar with it. Unfortunately it's not available at this time on your plan. I hope it won't be too expensive for you to purchase on your own. If you would like to work together I can find an alternative that is available on the formulary that you can get for your normal co-pay."

* When seeing a nondisabled person who is requesting I fill out an application for a disability parking sticker:

"Here's a copy of the form I will need to fill out. You can read the six criteria listed by the DMV that would allow a disability sticker to be issued for you. I'll step out and let you read it over. When I come back in we can review it together to see if you feel you meet one of the criteria listed."

* When asked to write a work note to excuse someone for a certain amount of time:

"I can't predict the future. I will give you a note that states you were seen and examined today, and with your permission, I will list a diagnosis and possible treatment. I can also state to a possible amount time your illness would be expected to last, but, the amount of time you take off is between you and your employer."

* When asked to write a note that "allows" a person to return to work after they had called in sick for a few days (usually these folks, for whatever reason, often don't have a good work history to begin with, thus the demand from their employer for such a note) :

"I can write a note that states you stated to having an illness for which you called in to work sick on a certain date or dates and that you saw me today and stated you feel you can now perform your work duties."

* When seeing patients who have poorly controlled diabetes:

"I'll be the first to admit that having diabetes stinks. It changes your way of life. Most of us go through life eating whatever we want, whenever we want and in whatever quantity we want. It's not easy to change your habits. It is up to you. I will help you in any way possible but the main treatments, physical activity and meal planning are things you will need to commit to do."

* Pain medications (narcotics) for chronic nonmalignant pain and other drugs of abuse-marijuana, etc:

"I'm will not get into a discussion on whether or not marijuana should be legal. At this time it is illegal. You have two options. If you decide to continue using marijuana you will not be eligible to receive any narcotics. If you agree to stop using marijuana and will take random drug screens, I will use all options available to treat your pain condition."

* When seeing patients who had a disability claim denied:

"I'm your advocate. I will always try to remain your advocate. However, I'm not involved in the final decision as to if you are granted disability benefits or not."

* Patients are upset their cold has taken 5-7 days to clear. They want antibiotics. They also don't want to use any OTC treatments to "mask" their symptoms:

"I'm the same way. If I'm sick on Monday I always except to be better by Tuesday. When I'm not I get mad. I hate being sick. However, when I have symptoms such as yours I always make sure to do everything possible to help my immune system. I get more rest, drink more fluids and use whatever symptomatic treatments are available to lesson my symptoms."

* When trying to help families understand why their loved one with dementia is running around yelling obscenities and trying to bite everyone:

"Have you ever seen someone when they are drunk? Some people drink and get sociable; they have fewer inhibitions, laugh and tell jokes. Others get drunk and become abusive; they look to get into fights, break things and may have foul language. Dementia can be similar. It lowers a person's inhibitions. Some folks are demented but sweet and sociable and will smile at anyone that walks by. Others are demented; shout obscenities, bite and try to spend as much time as possible naked."

* When trying to explain why a patient with dementia has become too disruptive to be kept on a dementia unit:

"I remember how surprised I was the first time I got called from a nursing home administrator saying a patient of mine could no longer stay on the dementia unit. I thought, are you kidding? What do you mean their behaviors are too disruptive?

Isn't that what your staff is trained to handle? Then he asked me one question. If you were touring a nursing home dementia unit for placement of a family member, would you consider a unit that has a patient shouting obscenities at the top of his/her voice?"

* When patients decline to have a recommended cancer screen test such as a colonoscopy:

"I respect your wishes. It's your decision. You're a smart person. It's always hard to know if you should do certain screening procedures. There are a lot of ways to leave earth. I've just noticed that having colon cancer is a crummy way to die. I had my first screening colonoscopy recently and everything went fine."

It's amazing to me how often folks then say, "Oh, I see, maybe I will go ahead and set it up…can you help me get scheduled for one?"

* When asked "Is it broken, is it broken?" (Usually seconds after walking in to see a person with bone pain that doesn't have an obvious deformity).

"I'm not sure yet…my X-ray vision doesn't seem to be working well today."

* When seeing a new patient who appears to be mad, pissed off, angry at the world or at the medical community in general:

"I'm sorry, have we ever met before? You look angry…I'll certainly try and do anything possible to help you."

* When asked if a specific herbal supplement (usually one I have never heard of before) will help with a medical ailment or condition:

"I'm not sure. Can you start by telling me about it and the research you did on the product?"

Usually, what follows is: 1. Read about it in a magazine 2. Read about it on the internet 3. My neighbor had the same problem and it helped

* When seeing a patient with a chronic musculoskeletal condition who is wearing a magnetic bracelet (usually on both wrists):

"Aren't the magnets supposed to cure these types of pains?"

* Why can't I get a good erection anymore?

"I don't know yet. I'll need to do an exam and possibly some other studies. In general, it takes 4 things in order to get a good erection. You need to have near normal blood vessels, an intact nervous system, a normal testosterone level and probably even more importantly, a normal brain. By that I mean you need to be confident in your ability to perform and you need to have a partner that also makes you feel confident."

* How can I remember which one is the good and bad cholesterol on my lab test?

"Just remember H (HDL) for healthy and L (LDL) for lousy."

* When a male in his 80's asks to have a PSA done (with no past history of prostate cancer):

"I will be happy to request the blood test but you need to be prepared to do something with the results. Many experts advise to not test over age 75. Autopsy studies show men who have died in their 80's of other medical problems have close to a 70% of having microscopic prostate cancer. If your PSA is elevated I will refer you to an urologist who may recommend a prostate biopsy. The procedure does entail some risk and potential complications. Sometimes cancer is found. If cancer is found the urologist might not recommend specific treatment other than watchful waiting. Then you might ask: why did I do the test in the first place? Think it over and let me know."

* Should I have Lasik Surgery done?

"I have some personal thoughts on the subject but I want to be as impartial as possible because you need to decide for yourself after weighing all the options. You need to consider it plastic surgery of the eyeball. You want to make sure you are seeing someone skilled in the procedure, as well as having it done at a center you have confidence in. I am told some centers are set up with a station system, often with groups of folks at each station. The last station, of course, is the one to determine if it will be cash, check or credit card. Some of the ads in the newspaper look like car ads...the use of different techniques based upon how much you want to pay...cost per eye...no money down...easy payment plans, etc. It's hard to argue with the success of the procedure, especially when Tiger Woods has it done one week and wins a golf tournament the next. But, there are risks. The risk, I believe is low. However, if you are in the 2-3% of folks who have a complication, it's 100% for you. I haven't had the procedure done myself but I do know a lot of people who have had it done and have done great. I also know a few who wish they never had the procedure done."

* Why do I have to do a clean catch urine specimen?

"You want to make sure you get an accurate sample without any blood from the surface or near the opening that could give a false reading. If you have microscopic blood present in the urine sample you will need to go through a series of tests, one of which includes having a scope put up your penis into your bladder. I'm sort of hoping I can go through life without having that procedure done."

I have found very few men forget to perform clean catch urines in the future after this brief discussion.

* Is it OK to have sex with a hooker in Amsterdam (I've had this question asked three times over the course of my career so far)? I go there for business and I'm told the prostitutes go through a physical exam every month and are checked for sexually transmitted diseases:

"Lets see. Say the girl you are going to be with was last examined 28 days ago and has been with about 8 men per working day since her last exam. Let's say she only works 4 days a week. So, with some simple math, you will be the 129th man she has been with since her last exam. How does that sound to you?"

* Can you fill out this disability form that needs to have a functional assessment done?

"I'm sorry but I will not be able to fill out this form for you. You will need to see a physical therapist with special equipment or a physician called a physiatrist. Most of us go through our day either sitting or standing; walking and lifting very light objects. Your disability form has questions such as in the midst of an 8 hour work day, what percentage of time can this individual walk on toes or heels, squat, crawl, kneel, stoop, bend, lift 0-4 pounds, 5-9 pounds, 10-14 pounds, etc. Obviously, I can't objectively answer these questions. I can give you a letter that lists your medical diagnoses, medications, symptoms and any other appropriate information."

* I won't take insulin:

"I can't force you take insulin. I recommend you do. Your high blood sugars are aging you internally quicker than your years on earth. In other words, your physiologic age is greater than your chronologic age. I won't abandon you as a patient if you decide not to start insulin therapy. I will still be your doctor. I will assist in helping you to see any other specialists needed for the complications of uncontrolled diabetes. Sometimes the eye doctor can delay the loss of your sight for awhile and the kidney doctor can help delay the need for dialysis."

I stole the above comment from a residency mentor years ago, Dr. T. Eugene Temple, Endocrinologist. It's still been effective over twenty years later.

* Why do I need insulin (for type II diabetes)? My pills have been working for years:

"It's the natural, almost expected course of the disease. I know it's disappointing. I wish the beta cells in your pancreas (that produce insulin) would continue to work for the rest of your life as well. Endocrinologists have found that most folks have already lost 50% of their beta cells when diabetes is first diagnosed. You need functioning beta cells for the pills to work. Insulin therapy is expected when you've had diabetes for many years. Sometimes there's nothing you can do differently to prevent the need for insulin therapy."

* I only drink 3 mugs of coffee/day, why is that too much?

"Most mugs of coffee hold about three to four cups. Most cups of coffee have about 100 mg of caffeine/cup. Most experts recommend we try and keep our caffeine intake under about 300 mg/day. Three mugs equal almost 10 cups. That means with coffee alone you are drinking close to 1000 mg of caffeine/day."

SIXTY-TWO: THE FIFTH VITAL SIGN

On Monday, a journal arrives with an excellent article for primary care physicians on the treatment of chronic nonmalignant pain (CNMP) with narcotics, when needed. That night, a segment of the nightly news reports all the recent robberies of a popular narcotic medication from local pharmacies.

On Tuesday, I attend a noon conference on chronic pain. The pain specialist describes an elderly female patient he follows with severe degenerative arthritis who takes about 1000 mg of sustained release morphine a day. She remains functional, with an acceptable quality of life, and has no side effects other than constipation.

On Wednesday, I receive a quarterly newsletter from my state board of medicine that lists all the physicians who have had their license suspended or revoked. A large number have been penalized for "indiscriminate prescribing of narcotics."

On Thursday, I meet a new patient who just moved here from another state. He is taking narcotics for CNMP. He agrees to sign a release for me to obtain his old records. He signs a narcotics contract. He agrees to perform random urine drug tests. He seems legitimate. He's a nice guy. I give him a prescription.

On Friday, I get a call from a local pharmacist to confirm the prescription I had written the day before on my new patient. He thinks the Rx was altered. I check my records. I had written for 90 pills. The patient tried to change it to 190 pills.

The treatment of CNMP isn't easy. Although this is true for most clinical areas of medicine, the use of narcotics conjures up thoughts of addicts and the criminal element. All physicians have been "burned" in the past. This causes hesitancy on the part of many physicians to use narcotics for the treatment of CNMP syndromes, even when indicated, despite our desire to help our patients.

Pain assessment is now called the fifth vital sign. It's the only "vital sign that is completely subjective. The range of pain severity for patients presenting with similar clinical symptoms can be broad. I hope I never feel 10/10 pain. By definition this represents "worst ever, unbearable, agonizing distress." I see patients daily who report 10/10 pain.

Pain management education, especially related to the treatment of CNMP, has only recently become readily available. Unfortunately, the treatment of CNMP was not a topic taught to most physicians who went to medical school prior to about 1990.

I've gotten more comfortable treating CNMP with narcotics, mainly through self study. However, I always use a narcotic contract and patients are informed that aberrant behavior will not be tolerated.

Don't allow treating the fifth vital sign to jeopardize your ability to practice medicine.

I'm hoping to practice for the rest of my career without having a television or newspaper reporter waiting to ambush interview me about "indiscriminate prescribing of narcotics."

SIXTY-THREE: TOOK A CHANCE

Pain threshold differs greatly for folks.

We are all wired differently.

Also, many times, there is a strong interface between chronic pain syndromes and mental health issues as well.

I had a very difficult patient for a number of years.

He had a handicapped van with a lift for his scooter. He drove himself to appointments.

He almost always reported 10/10 pain.

He would usually be upset with me, and my staff, if I was even minutes late for his appointment time.

One day, due to emergency, I was almost a half hour late in seeing him.

He was in an available exam room moaning, groaning and positioned almost like a pretzel in his scooter.

I was fairly certain his presentation was due to being upset I was running late and not due to an acute-on-chronic painful crisis. I took a chance:

Me: I'm sorry I'm late and that you feel so terrible. Let me see what I can do to help. Also, before you leave today please remind me to contact the DMV (Department of Motor Vehicles) about your condition.

Patient (who looked up at me, stopped groaning and moaning and uncurled his body from the chair on the scooter almost immediately): Why do you need to contact them?

Me (as sincerely as possible): Because of the pain you're in. I'm sorry your pain is so severe but obviously it's not safe for you to still be driving. It could be dangerous for you and for others on the road.

Patient (now sitting up straight in his chair with a normal tone to his voice): I'm feeling much better already. I don't know why I was feeling so bad for a few minutes back there. I didn't really sleep well last night but I feel fine now. I'm sure I'm still perfectly safe to drive.

Me: I agree. You look great now.

It was my most impressive bit of "doctoring" for the day.

SIXTY-FOUR: TWO OTHER CHANCES

1. I followed a relatively young female for a number of years. She was very demanding at times and would also be upset if she felt she was waiting too long to be seen, even when she would come in without an appointment, as was the case on this particular day:

One day I heard SCREAMING coming from my nurses office.

She was lying flat on the ground throwing what looked like a temper tantrum.

Me: I'm sorry you feel so bad. I'm going to have my staff call the rescue squad right away to come pick you up.

Patient (who immediately stopped screaming): Why are you going to do that?

Me: Because obviously you have something terrible going on that I won't be able to assess at this clinic.

Patient (now sitting up): I'm OK, I don't need to go to the hospital.

Me: OK, you do look better. I'll try to see you as soon as I can but you'll need to wait quietly in the waiting room until I have an opening.

Patient: OK, thanks.

2. I had another patient for a number of years who also hated to wait too long to be seen. Once he had an appointment at 3 PM but requested to be seen earlier due to wanting to "beat the traffic" home. I told my staff I would try to see him as soon as possible. Shortly after, a nurse knocked on my door.

Nurse: Mr. _____ just told the clerks out front he has taken five nitroglycerin pills waiting to be seen.

Me: Bring him right back.

Shortly after, I saw him in an exam room.

Me (poking my head in the door): I'll be right with you. I need to call 911 to have the ambulance come and get you.

Patient: Why?

Me (coming back into the exam room): Because you told my staff you took five nitroglycerins while in the waiting room. As you know, if you have chest pain, you should take one nitro every five minutes for up to three tablets. If you still have chest pain after three we need to activate the emergency rescue services.

Me: I'm sorry, I wasn't having chest pain and I didn't take any nitro's.

We then had a discussion about how behavior such as this could not be tolerated in the future.

He was apologetic. I did not "fire" him from my practice.

Continuity of care can be challenging, especially with adults who have chronic pain, emotional overlays and poor resiliency.

I had gotten to know these patients well over the years.

With all three I took a chance with my opening statement.

All three showed with their words and actions, after my opening statement, that a significant medical emergency was not present on this particular day.

Obviously if any of the three had failed to show such dramatic improvement, additional medical interventions would have taken place.

SIXTY-FIVE: THAT'S ABOUT ALL
FOR NOW FOLKS

It always helps for me to have certain quotes to read and reread to regain focus in my practice, as well as in my life.

Here are some of my favorites:

1. With God all things are possible.

2. It is what it is. My wife's favorite quote.

3. Yesterday is history, tomorrow is a mystery, and today is a gift (Eleanor Roosevelt).

4. Good instincts usually tell you what to do long before your head has figured it out (Michael Burke).

5. Stick to the fight when you're hardest hit, it's when things seem worst that you must not quit.

6. Choose a job you love, and you will never have to work a day in your life.

7. Whenever you get "knocked down" by life, get back up.

8. Health is not the absence of disease. It is the state of mind that lets one live a full, rewarding and productive life regardless of their physical condition.

9. The fact that life isn't always fair doesn't mean we shouldn't do everything in our power to improve our own lives or the world as a whole.

10. Life is not measured by the number of breaths we take, but by the moments that take our breath away.

11. One of the ultimate tests of being human is to be able to wish someone else well, even when you may be hurt. If you can do this, you'll experience the magic of the healing power of love.

12. Some of the happiest folks around seem to be the ones that are able to laugh at themselves.

13. The best things in life aren't things.

14. When you get used to responding in a more level-headed, calm manner to the small stuff in your day, you'll find that most things will work themselves out pretty easily.

15. What we have done for ourselves alone dies with us; what we have done for others and the world remains and is immortal (Albert Pike).

16. You don't have to explain something you never said (Calvin Coolidge).

17. Character cannot be developed in ease and quiet. Only through experience of trial and suffering can the soul be strengthened, vision cleared, ambition inspired and success achieved (Helen Keller).

18. Labor Day stands for America's greatest natural resource-not its minerals, its timber or its farmland, but its people: Americans who get up early everyday and go home tired every night, quietly creating a better life for their families and fellow citizens (Gerald Ford).

19. If you say something bad about someone, you will often discover that the same criticism applies to you.

20. Do not invest time in irrelevant details. It doesn't matter how well you polish the underside of the banister (Randy Pausch).

21. We cannot change the cards we are dealt, just how we play the hand (Randy Pausch).

22. It's not about how you achieve your dreams. It's about how you lead your life. If you lead your life the right way, the karma will take care of itself; the dreams will come true.

23. Qtip: Quit taking it personally.

24. You only have one opportunity to make a first impression.

SIXTY-SIX: ONE LAST MINUTE ENTRY

My daughter celebrated her 13th birthday this past June. My wife and I thought long and hard over what to get her. Her passion over the last few years has been horseback riding. We decided to buy her a horse (stable name-Dusty; show name-Sierra Dude) and to delay some home improvements we had been considering. I've attached a copy of a poem she recently wrote for her 8th grade language arts class. I think we made the right choice for her gift.

The Best Day of My Life-by Ellie Sheahan

I remember thinking this was just another morning before a show
Just like all the others
It just happened to be my 13th birthday
I remember waking up at 5am
Just like every other time
I remember fumbling with my tall boots and adjusting my belt in the dark so I wouldn't wake up my brother
Just like every other time
I remember how I thought both of my parents were driving me to the barn just so we could eat donuts together because it was my birthday
I remember being the first one out of all the other girls who were showing to arrive, since I like getting there extra-early
I remember when we started bringing the horses in from the fields
I remember I was trying to untangle Oreo's halter from Glee's halter when my trainer came up to me

I remember her saying that somebody bought Dusty and today might be the last time I got to ride him
She said some other stuff too, but I wasn't really paying attention after that
I remember I was trying not to cry in front of everyone
Then we went back in the barn and we finished feeding
It was all quiet except for the wonderful sound of horses munching, and Peppy attacking her bucket
I remember everybody was gathered down at the front of the barn
So I went down there too, thinking we were about to eat donuts and then load the horses on to the trailer
I remember then somebody handing me a name card and a stapler, and saying something like, "Can you go put this on Dusty's door? It's for his new owner"
I remember looking at the light green stall card
I remember reading it carefully
It had my name on it
I reread it a couple of times to make sure I hadn't been imagining it
I remember then I really did start to cry a little bit in front of everybody and didn't even care
I ran to Dusty's stall and put on his new card
It looked so much better than his old one
At that moment, my new horse looked like the most beautiful thing in the whole world
That's because he was
I remember I got Grand Champion in my division that day at the show, but I couldn't get any happier than I already was
It was the best day of my life

Thanks for reading!

Comments are always appreciated.

I'll continue to keep jotting down "interesting" stories from my practice and personal life in case I try to write book #4 in a few years.

Until then, my best of wishes to you and yours always,

Bill Sheahan